THE MEDIEVAL LIBRARY UNDER
THE GENERAL EDITORSHIP OF
SIR ISRAEL GOLLANCZ, Litt.D., F.B.A.

"He......rode up to the very dais" (page 128)

"Now is the duke come over the sea" (page 125)

Early English
Romances
Done into Modern
English with
Introduction and
Notes by
Edith Rickert

Romances of Love
Published mcmviii.

The title on the reverse of this page has been adapted by Miss Blanche C. Hunter from B.M. Harley MS. 2952, f. 126.

EARLY ENGLISH RO-MANCES IN VERSE: DONE INTO MODERN ENGLISH BY EDITH RICKERT: ROMANCES OF LOVE

COOPER SQUARE PUBLISHERS, INC.
NEW YORK
1966

Published 1966 by Cooper Square Publishers, Inc.
59 Fourth Avenue, New York, N. Y. 10003
Library of Congress Catalog Card No. 66-30732

Printed in the United States of America
by Noble Offset Printers, Inc., New York, N. Y. 10003

CONTENTS

ILLUSTRATIONS

INTRODUCTION

THE great age of romance in Europe coincides with the era of cathedral-building, the inception of both being in the eleventh century, their decadence in the fifteenth. To coincidence in time, due to no mere chance, must be added likeness of spirit—the same type of mind taking visible shape in words and in stone. In each form of art we find limitless aims, aspiration untroubled by consideration of fulfilment, gigantic ground-plans, un-bridled dreams, an ordered symbolism, a wealth of subtle, curious, monstrous, exquisite detail that ranged through human experience and imagination in its sub-stance—saints and devils, beasts physical and meta-physical, and all other things to be found in or over or under the earth. Each in its own way is a microcosm of that splendid, barbaric, restless, dreaming, subtle-minded, coarse-bodied, all but incomprehensible Middle Age between the Old World and the New.

Of this life, the modern verse romance, even at its best, as in the *Eve of St. Agnes* or the *Defence of Guinevere*, does not represent a tithe. Whereas the medieval production reflected the more truly, because so unconsciously, a multifarious life often grotesque, the modern is essentially eclectic, and sets aside deliberately all but the beautiful phases of that life. And where the old romance, like the cathedral, was primarily utilitarian, *i.e.*, was created for the intimate use, be it inspiration or amusement, of a great mass of people, the modern romance is decorative, and in so far as it is a deliberate imitation, appeals but indirectly as the reflection of a reflection of life, not touching deeply the present needs of humanity.

THE CHARACTER OF THE MEDIEVAL ROMANCE

In so far as it was made to be recited or sung, it was written chiefly in verse until printing was established, when it became, on the one hand, converted into prose for people who could buy and understand books, and on the other hand degenerated into the second-rate ballad for the illiterate. It was in the beginning intended for the upper classes—as the *fabliau, conte,* and *dit* for more mixed audiences—and was constructed with an eye to the character and taste of those for whom it was written. Therefore it is usually free from vulgarity, and tends toward a courtly tone. It is long, as designed to furnish continuous entertainment, and often divided into sections suitable for a day's recitation, sometimes with a brief résumé at the beginning, for the better understanding and remembrance of the story. Doubtless in a desire to make his tale last some while, the minstrel was led to spin out and expand indefinitely, to introduce subplots and counterplots, to vary its monotony with episodes relevant and irrelevant, to farce his matter with superfluous detail; certainly he developed the ingenuity of the juggler with many balls, in keeping the various parts of his narrative bravely aloft, and presumably a centre of interest in castle-communities. For the rest, unity, proportion, probability, logic, restraint, suggestion, were terms unknown in his vocabulary. He was content to swim in the current of his own events, attributing all sequence to happy chance, or, being devout, to the finger of God, and sure, we must suppose, of pleasing his audience by appealing to that quality of mind in which the age moved and breathed—that is to say, *romance*.

The Term "Romance"

It is needless here to recapitulate the warfare of scholars over the meaning of this term. Originally it was applied (1) to the French language, (2) to all matter derived through this tongue. But inasmuch as French, by virtue of its geographical and philological position, was the almost universal medium for transmitting tales from widely-separated parts of Europe and Asia, the enormous diversity of matter has led to some difference of opinion as to the essential element common to them all—if indeed such a thing can be found. But, at first glance, what is the likeness between the love-tragedy of *Tristram and Yseult*, the religious symbolism of the *Perceval*, Alexander's adventures among outlandish people and incredible monsters, the fairy-story of *Mélusine*, the fantasy of *William and the Werwolf*, the allegory of the *Rose*, and the heroic friendship of *Amis and Amiloun* ?

However widely these, and many others that might be named, differ in theme, plot, construction, and detail, they all agree in being as far as possible removed from the facts of daily experience. Each in its own way is exploring and exploiting some new field, be it in the world spiritual as in the visions of *Tundale* and *Owain Miles ;* in the world supernatural as in the tales of swan-maidens, giants, dwarves, elves, monsters ; in the world emotional as in *Erec et Enide, Eger and Grime*, and other romances dealing with love and friendship ; even in the world intellectual, as in the allegories. Only the world of Nature itself, for the most part, escaped handling by these medieval poets, being reserved for the great Romantic movement of the eighteenth century ; but even so, the Celts at this early time were awake and sensitive to many of its aspects, the English were not blind to the beauty of homely scenes, while even the Normans in the *Chanson de Roland* felt the splendour and the terror of Roncevaux, as appears in the haunting refrain :

> " *Halt sunt li pui e tenebrus e grant,*
> *Li val parfunt e les ewes curanz.*"

Briefly, the essential implication seems to me to be that of the soul leaving its customary habitations and wandering in strange places,[1] and essaying to bring into literature the fruits of its adventures.

THE EPIC AND THE ROMANCE

But, it will be objected, according to this definition, is not the *Beowulf* a romance, and the *Odyssey*, and the *Nibelungenlied ?*   And here we come upon the difficulty of drawing the boundary line between the romance and its predecessor, the epic.   Undoubtedly there are clear cases of each type, as *Apollonius of Tyre* and the *Iliad*, *Huon de Bordeaux* and the *Chanson de Roland*.   But how does the *Odyssey* differ from — say the *Pèlerinage de Charlemagne ?* To my mind, the difference lies not in the verity of the substance related, but in the attitude of traditional faith preserved in the epic, replaced in the romance by indifference to the fact and absorption in the wonder.   An epic is not perhaps much more credible than a romance, but it grows out of an age in which traditional faith is still sacred.   The romance is

---

[1] Prof. Saintsbury, in his definition of romance, includes an " immense and restless spirit of curiosity."

born of an age not incredulous, but so wildly credulous
that it accepts any hearsay as credible and therefore true ;
or, to state the point another way, the romance does not
limit itself to faith in the matters of national inheritance,
but scours the world for more wonders to be believed
in, assumes them as true, and proceeds to dwell upon
the marvel of their existence. Later on comes the
sifting process of the true from the false, the beginning
of realism.

To sum up, then, the epic, romantic, and realistic
attitudes of mind mark three stages of development,
when the subject for literature is (1) matter familiar by
experience or accepted through tradition ; (2) matter
but slightly familiar to experience, or tradition modified
by imagination ; (3) matter sifted out as true from the
accumulations of experience and tradition. Including
now the earliest of all forms of literature, the lyric as
the cry of a man's own passion, and the ballad as
voicing one man's account of others' passion, we find
that the progress of literature is from realism to realism,
with the epic and the romance as successive idealistic
phases in the accumulation of race-experience and race-
literature.

Further, as the process is continuous, so the types are
blended ; the ballad becomes transmuted into the epic
(as the lyric into the drama), the epic into the romance,
the romance into the novel ; and, while undoubtedly
many unmistakable examples of each class could be

grouped together, there are few ballads and epics without some admixture of romance, while some romances
are scarcely distinguishable from ballads, and others
have a strong epic tinge. The *Odyssey* is an epic because
even its most romantic episodes of the Sirens, Circe,
and Polyphemus were all matters of faith to the Greeks
for whom it was written ; so also is the *Beowulf*, in
which, such is the strength of traditional credence, the
Christian redactor himself explains Grendel as descended
from Cain. Even *Paradise Lost* is a true epic because
it handles a traditional theme in which the poet and
his audience had still complete and literal faith. On
the one hand, there are strong epic elements in some
of the Arthurian romances, especially the alliterative
Morte Arthure ; while, on the other, many of the French
chansons de geste,[1] more especially of Charlemagne and
of Guillaume d'Orange, have an epic foundation, always
tending to shoot up into the turrets and pinnacles of
romance.

THE ORIGIN OF MEDIEVAL ROMANCE

While the romantic attitude of mind has characterised Celtic literature from its earliest known be-
ginnings, more especially in regard to the natural and

---

[1] The word *geste* is used in three distinct senses in medieval
French: (1) deeds, heroic exploits; (2) the family or line
performing these deeds; (3) the history of the exploits of
this line.

I.

supernatural worlds and the emotional side of human experience; while Oriental literature seems always to have concerned itself with the forces of religion and of magic, together with the poetical aspects of nature; and while the romantic point of view is traceable in a fainter degree in the literature of the Greeks, Latins, and Teutons,—one of the most singular facts of history is the abruptness with which we find the accumulation of these qualities appearing in French literature in the twelfth century, then spreading with wonderful rapidity to Germany, Italy, Spain, Great Britain, and the Netherlands. There is a strong line of demarcation between the *Chanson de Roland* (1066–96) and *Perceval le Gallois* (*circa* 1175); and by no means is it conceivable that the earlier type should have developed naturally into the later without the introduction of extraneous elements. The progress is as follows: first, we find the epics, then suddenly the romances proper; then both continue to exist, side by side; and at last, the *chansons de geste* are slowly blended with romantic elements until they lose their original character and are scarcely to be distinguished from romances pure and simple.

The date of the introduction of romance into French literature can be set within a very few years. It coincides almost exactly with the reign of Henry II. in England. There is little of importance that can be placed earlier; and at the time of his death, thirty-five years later, the

first freshness and strength of the impulse had been
exhausted. Moreover, it would seem that it is the
Anglo-Normans, even more than the French of France,
to whom we owe chiefly the introduction of this new
quality ; hence, we must look into the history of this
people for the causes of their sudden inspiration. The
following facts seem to have a distinct bearing on the
case :—(1) King Henry himself, with his inheritance and
that of his wife, Eleanor of Aquitaine, added about half
of France to his English domain ; (2) in 1157, and at
intervals throughout his reign, he was conquering the
Welsh ; (3) in 1158, and again in 1166 and later, he
was subduing Brittany ; (4) between 1169 and 1185 the
Normans were establishing themselves in Ireland ; (5) in
1187 the Third Crusade was being preached, the Second
having taken place in 1147, seven years before Henry
came to the throne. Here is sufficient explanation of
the " lays " of Welsh and Breton origin, afterwards
worked up into romances, through which the Celtic
note seems to have been introduced into Anglo-Norman ;
while, on the other hand, the part played by France
in the Second Crusade and by England in the Third
suggests one way in which Oriental tales must have
been acquired. As to the matter of Greece and Rome,
no immediate occasion for its popularity at this time
appears ; but the fact remains that two great names of
writers concerned with antiquity, Benoît de Sainte-
More and Denis Pyramus, are connected with the court

of England, while Eustache de Kent, who wrote one of
the Alexander romances, was also English. The most
natural explanation for this florescence of antique
stories, in France as well as in England, seems to be
that under the fresh creative impulse stimulated by the
new matter borrowed from the Celts and the Orientals,
there was also a turning to the classic materials familiar
throughout the Middle Ages, and an endeavour to work
them up in accord with the new ideas.

But this new force in literature is only one phase of
an enormous activity of body and spirit which otherwise
manifested itself, especially in France and in Norman
England, in many wars political and religious, in the
building of castles and churches, and in those outlets
for superfluous energy devised at this time, the theory
of chivalry and the practice of jousting. This awaken-
ing may perhaps be attributed to two causes : (1) throughout Europe it succeeded a long period of petty dissension,
reaction, and mental torpor that followed the crumbling
of Charlemagne's kingdom ; (2) in England especially,
it was the natural result of the great mixture of races
(compare the conditions in America to-day). Within two
hundred years, we have Northman, Frank, and Gaul
blended in Normandy ; Norman, Saxon (Angle, Jute,
Dane), and Welsh (probably also some Irish and some
Scotch) blended in England, and mixed again with the
purer French of France. This is, I think, the deep
cause of this sudden spiritual wealth ; while to the

political and social circumstances of the times we may attribute the special forms of its manifestations in art and religion.

CHARACTER AND EXTENT OF THE FRENCH ROMANCES

At the beginning of the twelfth century, the poet, Jean Bodel of Arras, summed up the literature of his day as " matter of France, of Britain, and of Rome the Great." This classification indicates only the main lines of subjects in the period of enormous production between 1200 and 1500. Gautier mentions well over a hundred *chansons de geste* alone, ranging from about four thousand lines upwards, quite commonly reaching twenty thousand, and in the *Conte du Graal* drawn out to more than sixty-three thousand. *Ogier le Danois* exists in eight versions, *Huon de Bordeaux* has four successive sequels ; while the story that we know through Chaucer's *Man of Law's Tale* is related more than twenty times, often at great length, in all the chief languages of Europe, without counting various translations, and more than forty folk-lore versions preserved in modern form. These facts indicate somewhat the wealth of material saved ; and Gaston Paris says that incomparably more has been lost.

The same critic essayed to comprise all this vast accumulation under the heads : (1) *chansons de geste*, dealing with the national matter ; and (2) *romans*, dealing with (*a*) antiquity, (*b*) Greek and Byzantine tales, (*c*) Celtic traditions, (*d*) stories of adventure not to be included under any of the preceding heads ; but at the same time he admits that no such classification can be exact, in that we find romances sometimes belonging to more than one division.

The *chansons de geste* are again divided into three groups or cycles : (1) *la geste du roi*, or the national wars of the king, of which Charlemagne is the central figure ; (2) *la geste de Doon de Mayence*, or the wars of vassals against the king or against one another, wherein the centre of interest is gradually shifted from Charlemagne to the heads of various great families ; (3) *la geste de Garin de Monglane*, or the wars of the South of France against the Saracens, of which Guillaume d'Orange is the chief figure.

The *cycle royal*, of which the *La Chanson de Roland, Le Roi Louis*, and *Le Pèlerinage de Charlemagne*, all date back at least to the end of the eleventh century, consists of about twenty great poems, chiefly epic in character, but in a few cases with a strong element of romance, based more or less on historic foundations that go back to the days of the Carlovingians. The *cycle féodal* contains about as many vast compilations, but is believed to be more imaginary than historical, although some of its personages are known to have lived in the tenth century ; while the *cycle méridional*, again containing about twenty poems, celebrates the deeds, largely fictitious, for seven or eight generations, of the line of an historic prince Guillaume d'Orange, Comte de Toulouse, who died in 812, only two years before Charlemagne.   In addition to these three groups, which comprise about sixty poems altogether, there are nearly as many again, imitations, or variants, or extensions of the earlier works, which must be grouped with them because they belong nowhere else, until. at the end of the thirteenth century, we find in the *Charlemagne* by Girard d'Amiens, proof unmistakable that the impulse of the old heroic national literature had worn itself out.

Of the *romans* proper, those dealing with the " matter of Britain " are by far the most interesting and original. Early in the twelfth century a popular form of treating these subjects was the *lai*, derived in spirit if not in form from the productions of Celtic minstrels.   The *lai* is always short (usually under a thousand lines), generally episodic, and is clearly intended to be sung to musical accompaniment.

The relation of the *lai* to the longer *roman* is somewhat complicated and obscure.   Sometimes one was the source of the other, as in the case of *Le Fraisne*, which was amplified into *Galeran de Bretagne*, and *Eliduc*, into *Ille et Galeron ;* but again, the *lai* and *roman* seem to be independent growths from the same legendary root, as in the case of the numerous versions of the Tristan story.   While the original *lai* was almost certainly derived from Celtic sources (whether Welsh, Irish, or all three), as soon as the form became fashionable, it was used for classical and pseudo-classical stories, matter taken from any source whatever; but its popularity scarcely outlasted the century in which it was born. Indeed, it is doubtful whether it was practised to any great extent after the death of the famous woman-poet, Marie de France, who wrote half the *lais* which have come down to us.[1]

Among French romances, the *lais* are distinguished for their lightness of touch, their delicate descriptions, curt wit, neat turns of phrase, and whimsical fancies. Their art has the grace and charm of miniature-painting.

While some of the *lais* introduce King Arthur and his court, the great mass of Arthurian matter was very early embodied in a series of romances dealing with various knights of the Round Table, and in the thirteenth century combined with legends of the Holy Grail. Stories concerning the Round Table must have been current at least as early as the first third of the twelfth century; but the most popular romances of this group were composed by Chrétien de Troyes (fl. 1160–75) at the court of Marie de Champagne, step-daughter to Henry II. of England. He wrote of Tristan and Lancelot, Iwain and Gawin,[2] Perceval and Erec (Tenny-

---

[1] Two of these are represented by *Launfal Miles* and the *Lay of the Ash* in this volume; and two anonymous *lais*, by *Sir Orfeo* and *The Earl of Toulouse.*

[2] I use the spelling of the Middle English romance. This I

son's Geraint), besides in his *Cligès* making an effort to
graft Oriental matter upon the Arthurian cycle. Early
in the thirteenth century his work was continued by
Gerbert de Montreuil and Mennessier, who amalga-
mated with his story the Grail legend. The latter
was also treated at length by Robert de Borron, and
an unknown writer who turned his work into prose
about 1230. Hence, within a century of the time when
the historian Geoffrey of Monmouth first drew upon
the storehouse of Arthurian tradition for the literary
world of his day, this Arthurian material had been exploited in scores of elaborate romances, some of which
are lively in plot, vivid in description, and sparkling in
style, while others are thin, tedious, and prolix.

Contemporary with the work of Chrétien de Troyes
are the earliest romances of antiquity, such as the great
Roman de Troie, by Benoît de Sainte-More, who was
attached to the brilliant court of Henry II. Legendary
matter about Alexander the Great was worked up from
post-classical material, into at least five important versions,
several of great length, by the end of the thirteenth
century. There were likewise tales of Thebes, of Æneas,
of Julius Cæsar, and of various Roman emperors, historical
or imaginary.

hope to include in a later volume. It is the only one of
Chrétien's works of which a direct translation is preserved,
although the *Conte du Graal* is the source of various episodes
worked up more or less finely.

Another group of romances is directly traceable to the intercourse between East and West, initiated by pilgrimages and fostered by the Crusades. Sometimes the subject-matter turns upon the Crusades themselves, notably in the *Chanson de Antioche*, in its original form composed by *le pèlerin Richard*, who took part in the events related. Sometimes it consists of Byzantine or Oriental tales, borrowed, and in a measure transformed under Western influence, as *Dolopathos*, *Barlaam and Josaphat*, and others.

Aside from these various groups, there remain not a few romances which cannot be so classified. Several are Anglo-Scandinavian, as the French versions of *Horn*, *Havelok*, and *Guy of Warwick*; and still others are of doubtful origin, yet may not be included among the above-mentioned groups.

Notwithstanding important lines of cleavage between the splendid barbaric drone of the old national epics, the light fantastic trip of the *lais*, and the varied music of the romances proper, with their dreams of all things " in heaven above, or in the earth beneath, or in the water under the earth," there are certain fundamental qualities which set medieval French (including Anglo-Norman) literature apart from its contemporaries. It is the most original in transforming its sources, the most brutally aristocratic and feudal, and shows the strongest sense of form—this last a quality which even as early as the *Chanson de Roland* tends to artificiality.

TRANSMISSION OF THE MEDIEVAL ROMANCES

From France and Norman England in the twelfth century, romances passed in the thirteenth into Germany and Iceland on the one hand, and Italy on the other, arriving in Spain and English England in the fourteenth ; and after that time, strikingly after the common use of the printing press, becoming by degrees diffused and confused throughout Europe. A few words on the way in which they were handled may help to explain the fundamental differences between the French and English romances. In a state of things wherein every book was written individually instead of being produced in considerable numbers, each copyist of a text would not only insert his own errors, but would probably be beset by temptation to add his own improvements ; and further, where the recognition of an author was very often a matter of chance, there would be few if any protests against such alterations of a text. Moreover, when literature was published abroad chiefly by oral means, recitation or chant, the taste of the listeners would become an important factor in the handling of a text. An audience of fighting-men would demand bloodshed, one trained in logic would prefix subtle analysis, a fashionable gathering would wish to keep up with the ideas and metres of the day. A complacent minstrel would first alter his characters to suit the nationality of his hearers ; he might add touches of local colour, scenes with which he and they were familiar ; he might omit or extend accord-

ing to the life-experience or fancy of his patrons; he
might change the end of the story, or supply a sequel; he
might introduce veiled allusions to the history of some
great personage, who would thereby be flattered. He
might twist and pull out, and compress and chop and
patch his text, and so treat it in half-a-dozen ways that it
could not be always readily related to its original. Some
of these processes were deliberate, as alterations of names
and scenes, the addition or suppression of episodes, change
of metre, &c.; others were certainly unconscious, as the
introduction of northern scenery into a southern story,
medieval armour on classical heroes, middle-class manners at
a king's table. And so each redaction of a tale shows a spirit
and form differing more or less widely from every other.

Extent and Character of the English Romances

In England, Anglo-Norman romances flourished until
the time of Chaucer; English romances began to be
popular about half a century before he was born, and continued to prosper for about half a century after his death.
Therefore while the French romances were nearly three
hundred years in passing through their development, the
English, owing to circumstances forced upon them by
the Conquest and the slow amalgamation of races, had
scarcely more than half that time before the art of
printing began to turn them into prose.

Again, while the French *chansons de geste*, to a certain
extent, became blended with the *romances of adventure*, in

England old heroic literature was gradually but surely killed. It suffered first at the hands of Saxon monks, who rejected the most that was characteristically pagan, and then edited to their own purpose what remained. Afterwards, it fell necessarily into the hands of the middle and lower classes, among whom the English language was preserved ; and, in that the clerks as well as the nobles were chiefly Norman, the old English literature was not much understood or copied by them, was handed down chiefly by oral tradition, and in time, for the most part, disappeared. Hence, with some striking exceptions, the English romances either go back directly to a French or Latin original, or bear plain marks of having derived inspiration, if not actually detailed subject-matter, from the French.

The exceptions are, however, peculiarly interesting. Among them are : *King Horn* and *Havelok the Dane*, based upon Anglo-Danish traditions, probably independent of the French poems on the same themes ; *Guy of Warwick*, which seems to attach itself to a lost saga of King Athelstan, whereof an offshoot may possibly be represented by the romance of *Athelston*,[1] other branches having been preserved among the Latin chronicles ;[2] *Bevis of Hampton*, which may be German, but seems to contain at least a far-away reflection of the *Beowulf* story ; *Gamelyn*, *John*

---

[1] Included in Vol. II. of this series.

[2] Undoubtedly English poems on Offa, Wade, and various other early Teutonic heroes, known in England, have been lost.

the Reeve, The Story of Gray-Steel,[1] which show no marks of a French original, and are throughout essentially representative of the life of England in the fourteenth and fifteenth centuries.

The English romances are about seventy in number, and are usually much shorter than their French proto-types. Although the relationship between them and their sources cannot be always determined conclusively, at least seventy per cent. may be regarded as translations, more or less free ; a few are extensions or combinations of materials, as appears in the case of Chestre's *Launfal* by a comparison with two English versions, *Landavall* and *Sir Lambewell,* and with the French original ; and again, a few (notably *Sir Gawayne and the Green Knight*) seem to be what might be called improvisations on a French theme, and therefore rank as original work.

The oldest romance known which is unmistakably translated, *Floris and Blancheflour,* dates from the second half of the thirteenth century ; and soon after 1300 the practice of turning from the French became common, as is shown by the existence still of more than a score of romances written before 1350. The author of *King Alisaunder* (about 1300) illustrates the growing sense of the nation :—

> "French ken these gentlemen,
> But all Englishmen English ken."

In the second half of the fourteenth century, when this

[1] Included in Vol. II. It bears also marks of great antiquity, thoroughly Teutonic.

language had become established in court- and law-usage, sprang up the great mass of the popular romances which stirred Chaucer's fun-loving spirit to take them off in his *Sir Thopas*. And the fashion continued until well on in the fifteenth century.

Curiously enough, the flourishing of romance in English coincides roughly with the Hundred Years' War, as is indicated by the Auchinleck Manuscript at the beginning, and the Thornton and half-a-dozen others at the end. The significance of this agreement lies in the fact that this very period marks the rise of the middle-class townsman in politics and in trade, hence in wealth and social position. The rich citizen, as he progressed, demanded the arts; and so the drama for his convenience gradually moved away from the church and churchyard into the streets; song and story descended from the castle-hall into the market-place; and, in that their patrons had little incentive and probably less desire to learn French, both became English.

These romances therefore, with some important exceptions, are as different as possible from their French and Anglo-Norman predecessors, and bear essentially the stamp of the audiences for whom they were intended. They are shorter, because instead of whiling away winter tedium in a lonely castle, they are designed to catch the brief attention of a mobile and restless throng.[1] They

[1] About half of them could be recited well within an hour and a half; a good many, in much less time.

are ignorant of the splendour and ceremony of castle-life, but have as little sympathy with the barbarities of feudalism, on the one hand, as with the fine-spun analyses of sentiment on the other, which characterised earlier French literature. They are straightforward, robust in tone, fond of a fight, occasionally rough, with a sly touch of humour now and again, usually rather crude in expression, sound in morals, impatient of long imaginative descriptions, but given to slight suggestions of open-air life—indeed, they show very much the characteristics of the middle-class Englishman of to-day, who seems not to differ greatly from his fourteenth-century brother.

Romances of this description were largely the work of professional minstrels, who picked up their stories where they could, often borrowing freely from one to another, altering them as they thought best, according to the taste of their audience, and modifying them unconsciously in the light of their own origin and experiences, and so introducing local colour, character, and dialect.

In form, these romances of the professional minstrel are written either in short rhyming couplets, or in the popular twelve-line stanza of the day (rarely in stanzas of six, eight, and four lines).

Their style is marked by a sort of common currency of conventional expressions. Some of them contain as much as ten per cent. of phrases or even lines common to various others ; while a single conventionalism sometimes finds its way into fifteen or twenty romances, perhaps more. And again, each romance tends to develop in grooves, whereby the repetition of a thought or episode results in almost identical language, recurring occasionally three or four times.

The explanation of these facts seems to lie in the professional and commercial basis of this literature. Each minstrel was supplied with a stock of tales, probably derived and retained orally, and largely independent of written versions ; and when his memory failed, he could fill out gaps with stock phrases from his répertoire. The process is illustrated admirably in the two versions of the Northern *Octavian*, which display a multitude of slight changes, with subject-matter essentially the same. The result of this process is that all the poems of this class tend to draw together in a common degeneration from their original material.

This kind of tale-telling seems to have flourished especially in the Midland counties, and East rather than West. The examples included in these volumes are among the best that have survived.

For individual work, we must look to the minority of perhaps thirty per cent. These romances are not more or less homogeneous like the preceding, but break up into a number of small groups, characterised by difference of form, of authorship, and of locality, which as yet it is impossible to define with much certainty.

First, it is quite clear that the North Country, Scotland, Cumberland, Lancashire, and Yorkshire—the west more

I.

than the east—had its schools of poets ; and it is not impossible that one day we may be able to identify some of
them and place them more definitely, and give each in a
measure his due.   But at present it is safe to say only that
this district seems to have had its own fashion, as different
as possible from the larger group.   There are about
twenty poems characterised by a strong, sometimes ex-
cessive, use of the Old English device of alliteration.
Sometimes this is used alone, but again it is combined
with a fantastic and intricate rhyme-scheme, effective and
yet curiously artificial, almost pedantic.   These poems
are usually grim and martial in tone, showing apprecia-
tion of the wilder aspects of nature, and a strong power of
imagining and painting brilliant scenes ; they are usually
unconventional and unexpected in narrative, often force-
ful, with flashes of insight rare in the larger group.   Here
belongs the best of all English romances, *Sir Gawayne and
the Green Knight ;* and those most curious poems, *The
Adventures of Arthur at Tarn Wadling* and *The Avowing of
Arthur ;* the humorous fantasy of *Rauf Coilzear* (*Ralph
the Collier*) ; the ponderous *Destruction of Troy ;* three
alliterative versions of *Alexander*, and various others.

Aside from the two groups mentioned above, we seem
to find only the sporadic work of individuals : of that
patient good man somewhere in the south of England
who rendered into the same short rhyming couplet *King
Alisaunder*, *Arthour and Merlin*, and *Richard Cœur de
Lion ;* of Harry Lovelich, Skinner, who turned the great

Grail book into English; and of the equally much-enduring translators who gave to English *Ipomedon* (twice),
Generides (twice), *Partenay*, *Partonope of Blois*, *Clariodus*,
and other lengthy poems too copious for modern days,
and hence doomed to a small circle of readers, unless they
be first submitted to an extensive process of lopping and
compression.

It is interesting to note how in these individual works,
as in those much passed about by minstrels, the English
element crops out in the handling of materials. Common
sense, love of a good fight, of sport and the open air,
together with scorn of sentiment and hair-splitting, are
almost universally characteristic.

The only language, aside from French, upon which the
English romancers seem to have drawn is Latin. So the
Destruction of Troy must have been written by a scholar,
for it is taken from the Latin of Guido delle Colonne and
not from the French of Benoît de Sainte-More. Likewise, several of the Alexander poems, and a few works of
less importance, are derived from Latin sources. But on
the whole, the Latin materials are inconsiderable in comparison with the French.

Of the subjects chosen for treatment by the English
romancers, the Arthurian legend holds easily the first
place; and herein the figure of Gawain, especially in the
North, is more important than that of the king himself.
He is the hero of no less than seven romances, and plays a
large part in most of the five in which Arthur is ostensibly

the chief figure. Of the other knights of the Round Table, Percival, Lancelot, Iwain, Agravaine, Tristan, and Gawain's son, *Lybeaus Disconus* (The Fair Unknown), is each the hero of a separate poem.

The Arthurian matter was presumably derived from Celtic sources, how far directly, how far through the French, it is impossible to say; and there are a few other stories which seem to point to a Celtic origin, as *Mélusine* and *Lai le Freine*, while *Sir Orfeo* and *Partonope de Blois* are examples of the rehandling of classic myths in the light of Celtic fairy-tales.

Only eight Charlemagne romances have survived, including a fragment of the *Roland*. Doubtless, the period of the Hundred Years' War was scarcely a time for popularising, in English, French heroic literature. Of the eight, four have to do with Roland, chiefly as the opponent of the Saracens; and indeed, all but one (*Rauf Coilzear*), concern the wars of the Franks against the Mohammedans —a matter which might have been supposed to interest Englishmen as Christians.

The ancient world is represented by the *Alexander* and *Troy* poems mentioned above, all based upon pseudo-classical material; and also by tales which have nothing to do with antiquity beyond attaching themselves to figures of that time, as the Emperor Augustus (*Octavian*), Titus, Vespasian, Diocletian, and so on. *Ipomedon* borrows the names of the ancient Thebans for a story purely medieval, while *Partonope* renames and retells the story of Cupid and Psyche. Altogether, apart from the Alexander legend, which illustrated and was illustrated by travellers' tales from the East, and so became more Oriental than classical, the influence of antiquity upon the English romances appears very little save in a few isolated poems.

Such Oriental tales as were imported into England, *The Seven Sages* (two versions), *Barlaam and Josaphat*, and perhaps one or two others, came invariably through the French ; and, aside from the first named, seem not to have been excessively popular. But the infiltration of Oriental ideas is seen throughout the romance literature as a whole, although perhaps less in English than in French.

In regard to the subject-matter of the poems of English origin, the heroes seem to be ultimately Scandinavian, as in the case of *Horn*, *Havelok*, and perhaps of *Guy of Warwick* and *Bevis of Hampton*. *Gamelyn* is strongly local, but has also a Scandinavian tinge. A fragment of a cycle once attached to the name of Offa is preserved scarcely traceable in *Emaré ;* while Athelstan, once an heroic figure connected with Anlaf (the prototype of Havelok), survives in *Guy of Warwick* and *Gray-Steel*, and in the short romance of *Athelston*.

In actual value, the English romances vary enormously. Nearly all of those that arose in the North must be rated as having a distinct poetic merit, originality of treatment, and usually a good deal of interest somewhat blurred by crabbed dialect and eccentric style. Those due to the professional minstrels, on the other hand, are easy to read,

and so commonplace in plot and style, that it is necessary
to search for accidental graces of thought and expression.
Again, some are interesting from the standpoint of saga-
material; others, with small pretence to style, are good
stories; and a few have the strong interest which attaches
iteslf to the revelation of personal experience (here,
strikingly, *Sir Degrevant*, *Gamelyn*, and *Gray-Steel*, and
always *Sir Gawayne and the Green Knight*).

AIM OF THE PRESENT COLLECTION

In 1805, when the English romances were known chiefly
from Ritson's three volumes, Percy's *Reliques,* and Warton's
descriptions, Henry Ellis published an analysis, with occa-
sional quotation, of a number to which he had access.   His
book was published again by Halliwell, and has been for a
century a useful work of reference in regard to the character and contents of these poems.   During the past
century, practically all the romances have been edited;
but a number of them are not easily accessible, being in old
or rare editions.   The present collection will, it is hoped,
continue the work of Ellis in making this type of literature more widely known.   Instead, however, of following
Ellis's grouping of the stories according to the source of
the subject-matter, I have chosen and arranged them with
a view to showing their different ways of treating similar
themes. Thus Volume I. contains love-stories; Volume II.,
tales of friendship ; while, if at any time it seems desirable
to continue the series, Volumes III. and IV. would pro-

bably include stories of adventure, and " moral tales," which are often more entertaining than those which have no ethical or didactic purpose.

In translating, I have endeavoured to keep as near as possible to the spirit of the original. Whenever the word of the text is still intelligible, I have retained it, and have tried especially to avoid introducing expressions which did not come into English until after the date of the poem. On the other hand, I have often sacrificed archaisms to sense, but rarely or never picturesqueness of style to smoothness of rendering. It is my hope that, even in the translations, something of the peculiar flavour of each of the originals may have been preserved.

My thanks are due to Miss L. J. Naylor for assistance in this part of the work.

THE CONTENTS OF THIS VOLUME

The eight romances here included subordinate all interest in war, adventure, or friendship to a portrayal of love ; and in that, widely as they differ in some respects, they show a curious uniformity in their conception of this passion, we may suppose them to be fairly typical of the English attitude of mind between the thirteenth and fifteenth centuries.

The theme, then, with which they deal is of love unchanged by time and circumstance ; that endures all tests, all suffering, all humiliation ; that does all things and suffers all things for the sake of the beloved. The problem never arises from the mutability of human nature, but always from a conflict of changeless devotion with hostile environment. Floris seeks the world over for his sweetheart, and they vie with each other in self-sacrifice. The Lady of Faguell cannot survive her knight. The Princess of Hungary loves her squire in secret seven years and mourns him seven more. The Earl of Toulouse risks his life fighting for his ideal woman whom he scarcely knows. Launfal is punished a year long for betraying his lady's confidence, and loves her after she has brought him almost to the gallows. Degrevant risks his life daily for many months to see Melidore, and she defies the world for his sake. Orfeo mourns his wife in the wilderness for ten years, and finally braves Fairyland itself to win her back. Freine makes herself a servant to her lover's bride, seeking his happiness above all earthly things.

In quality this much-enduring love varies widely. If in the girl Freine we find the very ideal of self-sacrificing devotion, in the Lady of Faguell and her lover appears a morbid sentimentality which probably amuses us as much as it touched our medieval ancestors. The love of Floris and Blancheflour is faithful enough, but, except in the supreme moment of their testing, on no very high plane. On the other hand, the love of the Earl of Toulouse, though splendidly imaginative, is not sentimental; Degrevant is too good a fighting-man to be other than healthy-minded; while even the forlorn Squire makes a good show of arms when put to it. If Launfal is frankly

luxurious in his love, he at least has the excuse of having
to do with a fairy; and over against him we find Orfeo
with his touching devotion to his long-lost wife. If in
Freine love is an anxious and humble submission, in
Melidore it is a flame that burns away her fierce pride. If
we include the baser side of the passion as it appears in the
two knights that sought Beaulybon, in the treacherous
steward Maradose, and in the double-dealing Guinevere,
we may safely say that while with these English poets love
for the most part lacks the heroic quality of the sagas, the
brutal vitality of the *chansons de geste*, and the subtle over-
refinement of the later French romances, it is still shown
with a good deal of power, and with a fair range of circumstance, as an honest passion of the soul, making on the
whole for nobility, but with a distinct leaning towards a
sentimental view of life.

Floris and Blancheflour, the oldest romance in this
volume, is supposed to have been derived through the
French from Oriental sources; but no specific tale has yet
been identified. The Oriental element is of two sorts:
(1) the minstrel shows some slight acquaintance with the
Mohammedan law and with the life of the Saracens in
Spain, which, however, might have been derived from
French romances dealing with similar themes; (2) he
attempts an elaborate description of the wonders of
Babylon. A study of this material, however, shows it to
be so confused, that at one time the poet seems to be
speaking of ancient Babylon, and at another of Cairo

(Babylon in Egypt, more familiar, perhaps, than the former). And again, much of it is suggested elsewhere, here and there in the Alexander romances, and especially in the so-called *Travels of Sir John Mandeville*. Although this book is later in date than the romance, it is compiled out of earlier texts, of which one at least shows elements in common with *Floris and Blancheflour ;* and this fact suggests that an investigation of *Mandeville's* sources might give further results. In *Mandeville*, we read of Prester John's palace with pommels of gold above the chief tower and two carbuncles that give light in darkness ; and again of the mock Paradise of Gatholonabes, also called *Senex de Monte* [1] (the Old Man of the Mountain), with its wonderful garden full of strange trees and herbs of virtue, with all manner of beasts and birds, and wells set with precious stones. In this he kept always companies of fair damsels and youths under fifteen years of age.

Friar Odoric (before 1330) also has similar descriptions of the land of the great Can (*Khan*) and of this same *Senex de Monte*. He tells of a wonderful cistern with pipes and conduits that run through the palace, and of the gold drinking-vessels that hang on the pillars (see p. 24 of this volume). Instead of the Tree of Love, Odoric mentions the Well of Youth, which is replenished from Paradise. And finally, the Old Man has fifty virgins to

[1] He reappears in interesting fashion in Mr. Maurice Hewlett's *Richard Yea-and-Nay*.

give him his food as the Sultan in the romance has forty-four to take turns in washing his hands and combing his hair. Various other points of contact might be noted, especially perhaps the stress laid upon the good inns of the country.

On the whole, while an Oriental tale may have existed in regard to this Earthly Paradise, I incline to think that *Floris and Blancheflour* represents only a French story of young lovers similar to *Aucassin and Nicolete*, that arose probably in the south of France and was early blended with travellers' tales from the Orient.

The charm of the tale lies, I think, in the naïve solemnity with which the delightfully absurd situations are treated. The dialogue is at times surprisingly quick and natural ; and the quaint repetitions of similar phrasing for like situations, together with the gay colouring and the childlike simplicity of the treatment, make the romance singularly fresh and pleasing.

Sir Orfeo has been shown by Prof. Kittredge (*Amer. Journ. of Phil.* vii.) to be a working over of the Greek myth of Orpheus in the light of the Celtic fairy-story, the *Wooing of Etain*, which accounts for most of the variations from the ancient form of the tale. The point is the more interesting as this latter was known in Old English, and continued to survive among the learned throughout the Middle Ages. But the present version, with its happy ending, is distinctly of the people, and borrows little except the main theme and the names from the classical myth.

Its interest depends partly upon the vivid realisation of Fairyland, partly upon the sympathetic rendering of the love between Orfeo and his wife, and partly upon little realistic touches of wild nature and scraps of daily life.

The *Lay of the Ash* is translated from *Le Fraisne* by Marie de France, which seems to be the oldest version known of the superstition in regard to twins, combined with a love-story resembling that of Patient Griselda, made famous by Petrarch and Chaucer. It is generally believed that Marie used a Celtic source, but I am not aware that the probable character of this has been worked out in detail.

The poem is not as completely a love-story as the others contained in this volume, because the trouble and repentance of the guilty mother play an important part ; but, on the whole, the girl's sacrifice for love is the chief thing, and the little tale, mutilated as the English copy is, is far too touching and pretty to be omitted. There is a distinct attempt at character-drawing in the case of the mother and her faithful attendant, and the fussy old convent porter, not to speak of Freine herself. Moreover, the narrative is full of charming pictures : the flight of the girl across the moonlit heath, the convent at dawn, the porter's daughter nursing the baby back to life, and so on. To my thinking, the tale is a wonderful little bit of realism.

Launfal Miles may count as an original work, in that its author, Thomas Chestre, combined in it material from two French *lais*, *Graelent* as well as *Lanval*, the latter in the form of a shorter English rendering, of which several versions are still extant ; and not content with that, he added the quaint little incident of the mayor's daughter of Caerleon, who, it seems, had a mind to Launfal, and also, with more than questionable taste, he introduced the combat with Sir Valentine of Lombardy, which serves no purpose beyond that of showing how effective was the aid of Tryamour.

It must be admitted that most of the charm of Chestre's poem is due to his originals, upon which he by no means improved. The simple fact is, he had a good story to tell, wherein the element of suspense is so well managed that not until almost the last stanza do we know the hero's fate. It is upon the working out, then, of the plot (which Chestre weakened) and not upon character-drawing, or upon vividness of detail, that the interest depends.

The Earl of Toulouse, although probably translated from a lost French *lai*, seems to have been Germanic rather than Celtic in its origin. Dr. Lüdtke proved in his edition that it probably had an historic basis in a group of events connected with the Empress Judith and Count Bernhard of Toulouse ; but the facts had become sufficiently modified by legend before they reached the present poem.

To me its chief interest lies in its presentation of the love of the earl and the empress, which in its imaginative quality and self-restraint is almost unique in medieval literature. The hero is content to dream of her at a distance until her good name and her life are threatened, and then, convinced of her innocence, he puts himself into the greatest jeopardy for her sake ; while she, essentially true to her husband, faithfully shrives her of her only fault, that of once giving him a ring in pity of his love for her. Although the character-drawing is the chief thing, there are a few memorable pictures, such as the vigorous battle scene, with its allusion to the grief of the wives at home, and again, the earl's visit in disguise to the chapel, with the beautiful empress slowly revolving before him in order that he may see her well.

Sir Degrevant, for which no original is known, is to me one of the most interesting of the Middle English romances, too long neglected, perhaps, because of the crabbed dialect in which it is written.

While the names suggest that the minstrel had some French source in mind, certain features of the poem are so peculiar that we are forced to believe that it was taken not entirely from another romance or *lai,* in which certain conventional lines of conduct and episodes are always traceable, but in part, at least, from real experience. Now internal evidence and the date of the MSS. place the text at the end of the fourteenth century or the beginning of the fifteenth. The story is of a feud arising through jealousy between two great landowners in the North Country. This feud is initiated by the hunting and harrying of the knight's lands by the earl, and continues with a fierce battle in which the knight is victorious. Follows a raid upon the earl's lands by the knight in the way of retaliation; a love affair between the knight and the earl's daughter, who, at first scornful, is won by his prowess in a tournament; his visits to her in secret; his tremendous feats of arms upon the occasion of an ambush, after he has been spied and betrayed; and the final settling of the feud by his marriage with the earl's daughter.

The most singular feature of this romance is the connection of a hunting raid with a battle. Now historically these two events happened in the North Country, in conjunction, at the battle of Otterburn in 1388, between Percy and Douglas. Of the two ballads on this theme, the older, the *Battle of Otterburn*, makes Douglas the aggressor, while the *Hunting of the Cheviot* represents Percy as harrying the lands of the Douglas. Now *Sir Degrevant* tells of an earl with a castle by the sea, and of a knight who came " out of the west." If any identification with these two is possible, Degrevant must represent Douglas, whose lands were in Galloway (S.W. Scotland), and the earl with Percy, who belonged to Northumberland. In this case the romance would agree in its main course with the *Hunting of the Cheviot*, although in the immediate following up of the battle with a raid upon the earl by Degrevant is possibly a recognition of the other side of the story. Again, Froissart's account of Otterburn lays stress on the brave deeds of Douglas with his two-handed axe, when he is hard pressed by his enemies, while Degrevant also does terrible work with a sharp steel axe, and, upon a second occasion, with a two-handed sword.

These are a few of the coincidences that suggest some reflection of the battle of Otterburn in the romance (Halliwell first pointed out briefly " some slight resemblance,"
but did not develop the point), derived possibly not from
any ballad, but from actual experience. However, the
matter needs to be followed up. I am convinced that
while the love-story may depend more or less directly upon
some French source at present unknown, the battle scenes
are close to the life of the writer.

Another curious coincidence appears through the expression *Mappa Mundi*, wherein, says the text, we may
find Degrevant's name as one of the Round Table.
Clearly the author does not mean a " map of the world,"
but some chart containing a list of Arthur's knights. Now
in Winchester Castle there hangs to-day a great circular
structure which has been known for five hundred years at
least as " King Arthur's Round Table." On its margin
are painted the names of twenty-four knights. The fact
that Degrevant's name is not there is possibly explained by
the statement of a visitor in 1522, when the table was re-
painted, to the effect that some of the names had been
greatly corroded and were badly restored. If the form
Degrevant is found elsewhere, and is not a mere blunder
of the romancer's, it might easily have been altered into
Degore or *Dagonet*, which are there to-day.

There is further evidence in favour of *Degrevant*. The
Round Table at Winchester is mentioned by the verse
chronicler, John Harding (1378–*circa* 1460), whose asser-

tion " and there it hangeth yet," suggests that he had either seen it or heard of it directly. In his index, moreover, is the name *Degrevant*, in the list of King Arthur's Knights. This is the more interesting as the correct form *Agravayne* is not uncommon. The explanation of this double coincidence is by no means that John Hardyng was the author of the romance. Both style and form shut out this conclusion. And yet, singularly enough, the parallel can be pressed further. If the battle scenes seem to reflect the fight at Otterburn or a contest of that time very similar, as I believe can be proved, it is curious to note that John Hardyng was a North Country-man in the service of Earl Percy, and, although only ten years old at the time of Otterburn, must have had first-hand accounts of it; he actually took part in Homildon a few years later. Even more, Hardyng was a gentleman, a traveller, and a practical man of affairs, as well as a soldier; while the author of the romance was almost certainly a gentleman, a traveller, and a man of action, as far as may be judged from internal evidence. But at this very point come in the fundamental differences : Hardyng was learned in documents; the author of the romance, a minstrel, so little pedantic that he did not know the meaning of *Mappa Mundi;* and again, if the two chief characters can be identified as I have suggested, *Sir Degrevant* must have been written by an adherent of Douglas, not of Percy. Speaking with all due caution at this stage of the investigation, I believe that the author of the romance

I.

was not a professional minstrel, but a man of good position turned poet, perhaps not unlike his own hero, whose name he, as well as Hardyng, had perhaps seen on the Round Table at Winchester.

The poem is marked by a vivid imagination and a fierce vigour of narrative and description rare at any time, and especially in Middle English. A good deal of its force and brutal aptness of phrase has been lost in the translation.

The Knight of Courtesy and Fair Lady of Faguell is derived from a well-known French story, which was worked up into the long romance *Le Chastellain de Couci* in the thirteenth century. From the vagueness of the English author as to the details of the plot, and his confusion and lack of names, we may perhaps infer that he was not translating directly, but only retelling a story familiar to him in outline. The episode of the fight with a dragon he seems to have borrowed in order to fill in (it might have been taken from any one of several English romances), and he alters the scene and time of the tragedy from the Third Crusade to the siege of Rhodes in 1443.

The prototype of the knight was one Raoul de Couci, a poet, some of whose lyrics have been preserved. He accompanied his uncle to the Holy Land in 1190, where the latter was killed at the siege of Acre the following year. The uncle's tragic death was transferred to the poet, and connected with his well-known love for the lady of Faïel.

For similar tales of the eating of the heart, see Child's

Ballads, v., 29.   Perhaps the best known is the legend of
the Troubadour, Guillaume de Cabestaing.

The present poem is poor in everything but sentimentality ; but I have included it largely because it does
represent that aspect of medieval psychology, being a
singular combination of morbid hyper-analysis with sheer
brutality.   That point of view once granted, it is not
uninteresting.

The Squire of Low Degree is, as far as we know, an
original English production, though written by somebody
with an extensive knowledge of French ; but its sources
have not been thoroughly investigated.   In its main
theme, the long-continued devotion of the princess to the
supposed body of her lover, it is akin to the legend retold
by Keats in *Isabella, or the Pot of Basil*, with the important differences, however, that it is the headless body,
not the head, that she cherishes, and that in reality of her
enemy, not her lover.

While it is difficult to become excited over a story full
of manifest absurdities, wherein the characters are but
mouthpieces for exaggerated sentiments, the romance is
most interesting for its quaint and vivid pictures of
fifteenth-century life, and its curious lists of objects, such
as trees and plants, birds, wines, &c., which entered into
that life.   The little sketches of scenes such as the hunting party, the vesper service, the excursion in a barge, the
outdoor supper in the garden, and the going to bed are
vivid enough to enliven a far duller tale.

EARLY ENGLISH ROMANCES
IN VERSE

FLORIS AND BLANCHEFLOUR

THERE [1] was once a pagan king called Felis, who came out of Spain and crossed the sea in his ship with a great company of knights, and landed in Galicia. He was bent upon making a raid on the Christians, on gathering booty, and on burning their towns to ashes. A month and fifteen days he sojourned there, and every day he and his meiny issued forth to rob cities and bear away the spoils to their ships. There was not left an ox or a cow, a castle or a town, throughout that country-side; but it was all laid waste, to the great joy and delight of the pagans.

But at last the king bade load his ships, and summoned his pillagers to the number of forty knights, saying : " Arm you straightway, and leave the lading to others. Let us go up along the roads, and lie in wait for pilgrims as they climb the mountain-side."

[1] This opening to Floris and Blancheflour (as far as the word " commanded " on page 3, line 21) is supplied from the French. See note.

I.

This, accordingly, they undertook, and set upon the pious folk, who did not fight, however, but for the most part rendered themselves up in great fear.

And yet among them was one French knight, brave and goodly, on his way to the Baron St. James,[1] and with him his daughter, who had vowed herself to the apostle, and had come from her own country by reason of the death of her husband, by whom she was yet to have a child. Now this knight, loth to be taken alive, defended himself, and so was struck down and left dead; and his daughter was led away to the harbour and brought before Felis.

The king readily perceived by her face that she was of high lineage, and said that he would give her to the queen, who had prayed him for such a thing before he crossed the sea on his raid.

Presently they entered their ships, raised their sails on high, and with a fair wind returned home rejoicing, and within two days were in their own country, and went ashore, the king with his baronage. Word of his arrival had come before him to Naples,[2] and the townsfolk issued forth to meet him with great merry-making on all sides. Thus he entered the city, and dealt out the plunder with great largess among his barons. For his own part, he gave the captive woman to the queen, who received her with

[1] Of Compostella, in Galicia, Spain. A famous medieval shrine.

[2] Apparently thought to be in Spain.

great joy, and led her away to her own chamber, where she
was guarded well, according to the heathen law,[1] and well
served and honoured.

Often the queen talked with her, and jested, and learned
French; and the woman herself was so gentle and so
courteous that she was loved by all and served as honourably as the queen herself.

One day as she worked in the chamber at a standard for
the king, whereon were broidered himself and his queen,
she grew pale and trembled, and pressed her side and
groaned often, like one in great pain, as indeed she was.
And when the queen asked the cause of this, she found
that they two were to have children at the same time.

Accordingly, on the flowery day of Easter, a boy was
born of the pagan queen, and a girl of the Christian
woman; and the two babes were named from that
feast-day, the little girl Blancheflour, and the king's son
Floris.

Now the king and queen trusted their child to the fair,
wise Christian woman to care for and govern in all things,
save that the nurse was a pagan, as their law[2] commanded.

In all that land were no fairer children than these, whom
the Christian brought up until they were seven years of
age, loving each full as well as the other.

Then one day as the king looked at his dear son, he said

[1] A suggestion of the harem (?).
[2] Mohammedan.

it were a great pity save the boy were set to learn letters in
the books, as do men alike of high and low estate.

" Fair son," said he then, " now must thou be learn-
ing ; look thou do it willingly."

But Floris wept as he stood before the king : " Shall not
Blancheflour learn with me ?   I cannot go to school without Blancheflour ! "   And he said again : " I cannot read
or sing in any school without Blancheflour ! "

Then the king answered : " She shall learn for love of
thee."

So they were put to school, and both were so good of
wit that it was a wonder to see their lore.   But yet was it
more wonder to see their love, which was so strong that
they might never be parted asunder.

After they had gone to school five years, they had learned
so well that they knew enough of Latin, and could write
readily on parchment.[1]   But the king, perceiving the great
affection between them, thought that it would not grow less
when they were of age, and that he might not be able to
withdraw Blancheflour's love when Floris should take wife
according to the law,[2] so he spoke to the queen, and told
her of his trouble as to how Floris would fare.

" Dame," he said, " by my counsel, Blancheflour must
die !   When that maid is slain and brought out of her life-
days, as soon as Floris becomes wiser, he will forget her,
and then he will marry to our liking ! "

[1] See note.   [2] Mohammedan.

The queen answered him, as thinking by her counsel to save the maid from death : " Sir," she said, " indeed, we must devise that Floris live as our son ought to do, and not lose his honour for that maiden's sake ; but I hold that to steal her away, so that she might come by her death afterward, were more fitting than to slay her outright ! "

The king could not but grant that this was so, and said : " Dame, counsel us what is to be done."

" Sir, we must send Floris into the land of Mountargis.[1] My sister, the lady of that country, will rejoice ; and when she knows for whose sake we have sent him away, she will do everything in her power, day and night, to make his love of Blancheflour as it had never been.   And, sir, I rede that the maid's mother say that she is sick, and therefore the child may not leave her."

Now are these children so heavy-hearted because they may not go together, that sadder little ones were never seen.

Floris said, weeping, to the king : " Sir, verily ye send me away to mine own damage, now that she may not go with me !   Since we may not be together, all my joy is turned to sorrow ! "

But the king said : " Son, within this fortnight, be her mother quick or dead, verily the maid shall come to thee ! "

[1] In Loiret, central France.

"Yea, sir," he answered. "I pray you it be so! If ye send her to me, I reck never whither I wend."

When the child had granted this, the king was glad, and entrusted him to his chamberlain. They went with all the state befitting a king's son, and were well received by Duke Orgas,[1] the lord of that castle, and his lady. But however blithe they were to see Floris, he thought ever on Blancheflour; nor would any game or glee divert him since he might not look upon her.

His aunt hath set him to book, with other lads and maidens a many that came thither for that; but he only sighs and learns nothing, ever mourning Blancheflour. Howsoever any man speak to him, love is so rooted in his heart that he finds nothing so sweet—nor galingale [2] nor liquorice—as is her love. So much he thinks on her, that one day when he seeth her not seems as long as three.

Thus he abides in great trouble the fortnight, and when he perceives that she is not come, so heavy is his sorrow that he cares for neither meat nor drink, nor partakes thereof.

The chamberlain sent the king a letter to tell of his son's estate; and presently the king broke the wax for to know what it said. Quickly his mood changed, and he understood, and full of ire sent for the queen, and told her how he was vexed, and said in his anger:

[1] See note.

[2] An aromatic East Indian root much loved in the Middle Ages.

" Let that maid be brought forth, and her head shall from her body ! "

The good queen was sorrowful, and said : " For God's love, sir, mercy ! At the nearest haven are come rich chapmen, merchants from Babylon, that would gladly buy her. Thus may ye have for her much goods and chattels, and soon she will be taken from us without that we slay her ! "

Scarce would the king grant this, but so it fell out. He let send after the burgess, a civil, kindly man, who knew all about buying and selling, and had many languages in his mouth.

To him presently was the maid delivered, and so brought to the haven, where she was sold for twenty golden marks, and the richest cup in all the world and the best carven. He that wrought it was no fool, for it portrayed how Paris led away the queen, and on the covercle was the love of those two, and on the knob stood a carbuncle [1] so brilliant that in the deepest cellar in the world it would light the butler to draw his ale and wine. Of silver and good fine gold.[2] . . . The noble King Æneas won it at Troy in battle, and brought it to Lombardy and gave it to Lavinia his love. A thief afterwards stole it from the treasure-house of King Cæsar, and that same thief gave it for Blancheflour, knowing well that if he might bring her into his country, he would win three such.

[1] See note.   [2] Gap in MS.

Now these merchants sailed away with the maid to their own land, and journeyed till they came to Babylon, where they were soon at one accord with the emir [1] to sell her to him ; and he bought her for seven times her weight in gold as she stood, for he thought to have her for his queen one day, and accordingly placed her honourably among the maidens in his tower.   Well might these merchants depart contented with their bargain !

Now leave we Blancheflour and return to the land of Floris.   The burgess came back to the king with the gold and other fee, and yielded up to him alike the money and the cup.   And the king made to build in a church a very fair tomb, and let place above it a new-painted stone, with splendid letters written all round about it.   For him that might read, they spoke and said—

> " Here lieth sweet Blancheflour,
>   That Floris lovèd par amour."

Now Floris himself had set out to return to his father's land, and presently dismounted in the hall and greeted fair the king and queen.   This scarcely done, he asks where might be his sweetheart, and awaits no answer, but hastens away to the bower to the maid's mother, and asks again : " Where is my sweet Blancheflour ? "

" Sir," she answered, " of a truth I know not where she is."   For she remembered her of the lie that was ordained by the king.

---

[1] Text: *admiral*, an older form for *emir*.

"Thou art befooling [1] me!" he cried; "and thy jesting is grievous! Tell me where she is!"

Then she answered, all in tears, "Sire, she is dead!"

"Dead?" quoth he.

"Sire, yea, of a truth!"

"Alas, when died my sweet thing?"

"Sire, within this sevennight the earth was laid upon her; and she died for love of thee!"

Then gentle Floris fell a-swooning on the pavement; and the Christian woman began to cry out on Jesu Christ and St. Mary.

The king and queen hearing her, ran into the bower; and there the queen beheld her child thus a-swoon, and the king was sorrowful to see how his son fared for love.

When he awoke and could speak, he wept and sighed bitterly, and besought his mother: "Dame, take me where the maid lieth!"

They brought him thither, near dead for love and sorrow. And when he came to the tomb, and read the letters that say—

> "Here lieth sweet Blancheflour,
> That Floris lovèd par amour,"

three times he swooned, and might not speak at all. But presently, when he found words, with bitter weeping and sighing he began to bemoan her, and his tears fell thick as a shower of rain.

[1] See note.

" Blancheflour," he said, " Blancheflour, the sweetest thing in any place! Of high lineage wert thou born.[1] . . . In all the world is not thy peer among women! Enough thou wist of books and of all courtesy ; and great and small alike loved thee for thy beauty and goodness! If death were dealt out justly, we should have died on the same night, as in one day we were born ! We should have died together ! O Death, full of envy and all treachery, thou hast robbed me of my dearest—to betray folk is thy wont ! If any man would live, thou wouldst it not ; and fain would I die, and thou wouldst it not ! Whither I would that thou come, there wilt thou no whit ; and whither I would thou come not, there comest thou enough ! He that boasteth him of life is thrust under the rib by thee ; and if any worn-out wretch cares naught for his life and fain would die of old age, on him wilt thou not glance ! I will no longer live out my life ; I will be with her ere the night ! I will cease to call upon death, and will make an end of my days ! "

As a man that would slay himself, he drew his hanger out of its sheath, and had smitten it into his heart had not the queen, his mother, perceived and fallen upon him, and reft him of his little knife, whereby she saved him.

All weeping, she ran forth and found the king and said : " For God's love, sir, mercy ! Of twelve children we have none left alive but this only ; and it were better

[1] Gap in MS.

that Floris sat mournful, he said to him : " Child, methinks
thy thought is much on thy chattels."

" Nay, sir, I think not on chattels, but on another
thing."

Then said the master of the inn : " Thus sat here, the
other day, fair maid Blancheflour. Alike in hall and
chamber she was ever grieving, and bewailing Floris,
her dear friend ; and she so lamented that she had no
peace ! "

When Floris heard tell of his sweetheart, he was blithe
and had fetched a cup of white silver, and a mantle of
scarlet, cross-barred with miniver,[1] and gave them to his
host. " Have these," he said, " to thine honour ; and for
them thou hast Blancheflour to thank ! She was stolen
from my country, and now I go my ways seeking her.
Well might he gladden my heart that could tell me
whither she was led ! "

Then said that good burgess : " She was taken to
Babylon, where the emir hath bought her."

Now Floris goes to bed, but hath no rest for thinking all
the while on Blancheflour, until at last dead sleep overcame him.

On the morrow as soon as it was day, he took his leave
and went forth, giving his host for the night's lodgement
an hundred shillings. And earnestly the child besought
the burgess to help with his counsel if he had a friend in

[1] Grey fur.   Squirrel (?).

Babylon that might show and advise how by some means
Blancheflour might be won away.

"Thou shalt come presently to a bridge, and find the
warden thereof at one end where his palace stands; he is
a courteous man and kind, and my sworn brother,[1] and he
can counsel thee well. Bear him this ring as a token from
me, so that in all ways he shall help thee as he would
myself."

Thereof Floris is blithe, and thanks his host heartily,
and, taking the ring, abides no longer, but says farewell;
and by high undern [2] he is at the bridge.

When he arrived there, he found the warden at one end,
sitting on a marble stone, a very goodly and gracious man
whose name was Dayre.[3]

Floris greeted him courteously, and gave him the ring,
and by that token put himself into the burgess's charge;
and he had there fair entertainment, so that they were all
blithe and merry that sat in the hall.

But ever Floris sighed bitterly until at last Sir Dayre
observed him: "Dear child, what ails thee, that thou art
so pensive? I ween thou art not in good company, to
make such doleful cheer, or thou likest not this inn?"

Then Floris answered him: "Sir, i' God's mercy, I had
never before so good entertainment! May Our Lord
grant me to live until I can requite thee! But I think
now, sir, in one way or another, of my merchandise, lest I

<hr>

[1] See note.   [2] Mid-day.   [3] From Darius, doubtless.

find not in the beginning that for which I am come hither. And this is my greatest fear, that I may find it and still must let it go ! "

" Child," said that noble burgess, who was alike courteous and friendly, " fain would I help thee and teach thee to come into better estate.   If thou shouldst tell me thy grief, I would gladly lend thee my counsel ! "

Beginning and end, he hath told him how Blancheflour was stolen away, and how he was a king's son come hither for love of her to win her back.

But Dayre held Floris for a fool.   " Child," he said, " I wot thou get thy will !   Thou seekest thine own death ! At the emir's banquet will be an hundred and fifty great kings, but none of them durst undertake such a deed as to win this maid by strength or by guile !   The bare thought of it would nearhand kill the emir !   And Babylon,[1] as I know, is sixty miles round about, and hath on its walls seven times twenty gates, with twenty towers therein ; and every day in the year is there such cheaping [2] as is in full fair-time !   In that town are seven hundred towers and two, and the weakest of all would challenge the emperor himself to enter by force or by trick.   Though all men that are born had sworn by their eyes to win that maid, they would get her as easily as the sun and moon from heaven !

" Right amid the burg stands a strong tower an hundred

---

[1] See note.   [2] Buying and selling.

fathoms high and even so wide, and proudly built of lime and marble stone. There is none other like it in the world, with mortar so well made that it will not break for steel or iron. On this tower are battlements of silver and crystal, and the pommel [1] above the leads is wrought with great skill; and high above is a carbuncle-stone that gleameth ever. There is no such other, for it shineth like the sun by day, and there is never so dark a night that torch or lantern needeth to burn in the chambers. And in the tower is a very clear well that runs into a pipe of brass when there is need; from floor to floor in great streams it rushes from bower into hall. In that high dwelling are four and forty maidens; and the man that came among them would never wish for Paradise! [1] There be sergeants on each story, eunuchs all, to serve these nobly-born maidens; and at the gate is a warder that is neither fool nor coward; and if any man come within the barbican but by his leave, he will be beaten and eke robbed. It is a proud porter, and every day he walks along the wall.

"And the emir is such a man that year by year he takes a new wife, even though he love his queen as dearly as himself. From the upper story men bring down all the maidens of rank, and lead them into the fairest orchard that is in Middle-Earth. [1] All about it is a wall of splendid crystal—a stone wherein [1] men may see much of this world's wisdom; and there are bird-notes so gay that men

[1] See note,

might live among them for ever.   A well springs within, quaintly wrought : the streams, I may say, come from Paradise ; the gravel is all precious stones of virtue, sapphire, sardonyx, chalcedony, jacinth, topaz, onyx, and many another that I cannot name.   Above the well stands a wonder fair tree called the Tree of Love, which bears leaves and blossoms alway ; for as soon as the old be done, the new spring in their places.   Under this tree are brought all these maidens, and she on whom falls the first flower shall be honoured as queen.   The spring is of so much dread that if any maid unchaste step to the ground to wash her hands, it welleth up like mad and turneth from water to blood, and so rusheth upon her that she is undone, but those that be chaste maidens may wash there, I ween, for the water will run fair and clear and do them no danger. If there is any maiden that the emir loves best, on her shall the flower be made to fall by conjury and enchantment. So he chooses his wife, and now all men deem that it shall be Blancheflour."

Three times Floris swooned there ere he might find tongue, and when he awoke, he said, with bitter weeping and sighing : " Dayre, I shall die unless thou help me ! "

And Dayre answered : " I see full well thou art bent upon thy death ! Floris," he said, " dear friend, the best counsel I can give thee is to go to the tower to-morrow as though thou wert a good engineer. Bear with thee a square and a plan in the guise of a good mason. Study the height of the tower, and with thy foot pace out the breadth. The porter is false and evil, and will at once argue with thee, and charge thee with being a spy. Answer him gently, and speak with him courteously, and say thou art come from far away to try to build a tower after this plan in thine own country, if thou be spared so long. When he hears thee speak so graciously and answer him so mildly, then will he come thee near and bid thee play with him at chess.

" When the chess-board is brought forth, play not without pence, but have ready in thy pocket twenty marks. If thou win aught of him, hold it of little account, but if he win aught of thine, leave with him all thou hast. Much he will thank thee and be greatly a-wondered of thee ; but he is so covetous and eager for chess that he will pray thee come to-morrow to play. Grant him this, and take with thee to-morrow twice as much, and ever keep by thee thy golden cup. And on the third day, bear forty pounds and thy cup again. Earnestly he will bid thee to stake the cup ; but answer him at first that thou art weary of play. I wot every day he will honour thee as much as he can, and will take thee to his lodging to win the cup of thee. He will covet it mightily and be anxious to buy it, and he will offer thee much to this end. But thou shalt give it to him blithely, though it be of pure fine gold, for I wot that he may help thee most of any in thy need. Say thou hast no lack of gold and silver and possessions, and that thou wilt

share with him so that he shall be a rich man for ever ;
then will he be glad, and begin to love thee, and fall at thy
feet and offer to become thy man.   Thou shalt take pledge
of him, and make him swear to do thee all the service that a
man should yield to his lord.   If thus thou win his love, he
may help thee with some device ; for then thou mayst
reveal thyself and show him thy secret."

And so Floris did as Dayre taught him, and through the
cup and other fee the porter became his man.   " Now,"
said the child, " thou art sworn, and all my trust is in thee,
wherefore thou must needs give me help, for without thy
service I may not speed ! "

Beginning and end, he told him how that maid was
stolen away, and how he was a king's son of Spain come
hither for love of her, to try with some device to win
her back.

When the porter heard this, he sighed, saying : " I am
justly betrayed through thy chattels, and in fear of my
life, for I know now how it goeth, and through thee am
like to suffer death.   Nevertheless, I will not fail thee
while I live ; whatsoever betide me, I shall keep all the
foreward.[1]   Return thou, Floris, to thine inn while I be-
think me of some device.   Between now and the third day
I will try what I may do."

Floris sighed and wept, as thinking this term long ; but
the porter found a thing to do.   He let flowers be gathered

[1] Agreement.

in the meads, and baskets be filled to strew in the maidens'
bowers ; and in one of these he put Floris. Two giggling
wenches bare it, and for its weight were wroth, and bade
God send him an evil end that had put so many flowers
therein.

They did not well understand that they should bear the
basket to Blancheflour's bower, but turned to the left, to
another chamber, not hers, and set it down there ; so went
forth and left it standing.

Now a maiden came to look at the flowers and play with
them ; and Floris, thinking this would be his sweetheart,
leaped out of the basket, whereupon she gave a cry, and
shrieked in fear.

When Floris saw that it was another, he held him for
lost, but crept back into the basket again, and hid among
the flowers.

Now maidens came a-running thither, well fifteen in a
throng ; and they asked what ailed her to make such outcry. But she thought the child might be Floris, for her
chamber was nigh Blancheflour's, and they were seldom
not together, and she had often heard how Blancheflour
had been sold away from him ; so she answered her
women and sent them away : " I came up to the basket to
look at these flowers and play with them, and ere I wist, a
butterfly had fluttered out into mine eye ; and I was so
sore affrighted that I shrieked ! "

Thereupon the others laughed, and made sport of that

sweet maiden Claris; and presently they went away again and let her be. But she ran into Blancheflour's chamber, crying: "Dear Blancheflour, wilt thou see a pretty blossom? It grew never in this country the flower that I shall put into thy hand!"

"Away, Claris!" quoth Blancheflour. "It doth thee little honour to mock at me! He that loves *par amour* and is happy, may care for flowers; but I ween, Claris, without jest, that the emir will have me to wife. And that day shall never come, nor shall any twit me that I am faithless, and change old love for new, as doth Floris in his land! Since I may not have him, none other shall get joy of me!"

When Claris heard of all this sorrow and the constancy of this troth, tears fell down her face. "Blancheflour," she said, "sweet friend! Leave off, sweet Blancheflour, and come and see this fair blossom!"

They went in together, and Floris, who had heard all that they said, leaped out of his basket and ran to Blancheflour. Each knew the other well and changed hue, and without a word they sprang into each other's arms, and kissed and wept together. Their kissing lasted more than a mile,[1] and even that seemed to them but little time.

Claris beheld their demeanour and their joy, and said, laughing, to Blancheflour: "Fellow, knowest thou at all this blossom? A little erewhile, thou wouldst not look at

[1] While a man might run more than a mile.

it, and now thou canst not let it be ! She must know much
guile to whom thou wouldst give a share thereof ! "

" Of a truth," quoth Blancheflour, " this is mine own
dear Floris ! "

Now both these two sweet things, weeping, cried her
mercy, not to betray them to the emir, for then were they
sure to die; and she had pity of them : " Doubt ye
nothing, no more than had it befallen myself ! Know ye
well, I will hide your love ! "

Thereafter, she brought them to a bed of pall and silk,
and so left them together.

Floris was first to speak : " Our Lord that madest man,
I thank Thee, God's Son, that I am come to my love !
Sweetheart, now I have found thee, all my care is away ! "

Now have they told each other of the sorrow and bitter
woe that each hath suffered since they were parted; and
they embraced and kissed and had great joy together.
And Claris served them in secret so well that they asked
no other heaven than alway to lead such life. But presently, alas, they were discovered !

It was the emir's wont that every morning two maidens
should come out of their chamber to serve him up in his
tower. One should bring comb and mirror, and comb his
head with all state ; and the other, towel and basin
wherein to wash his hands. And every day he was served
by a fresh pair ; but those that went most often were
Claris and Blancheflour.

Claris—blessings on her !—arose one day in the morning
and called her mate to go with her into the tower. Quoth
Blancheflour : " I am coming ;" but she said it in her sleep.

So Claris went alone, and anon the emir asked for
Blancheflour.

" Sire," she answered, " she hath wakened all the night,
kneeling and reading in her book, and praying God's blessing on thee that thou mayest live long ; and now she is
asleep and may not come to thee ! "

" Is that truth ? " he asked.

She said : " Yea, sire, beyond a doubt."

" She is a sweet thing," said he.   " Well ought I take to
wife one that prays so well for me ! "

On the morrow when Claris arose, she blamed Blancheflour for making such long delay. " Arise," she said.
" We must go together."

Quoth Blancheflour : " I come anon."

But Floris began to embrace her, and she him, un-
wisely ; and so they fell asleep again.

Claris came to the pillar,[1] and took the gold basin, and
again called Blancheflour to go up with her ; and when she
answered nor yea nor nay, Claris thought she was already
gone.   But she was not in the tower, and the emir presently asked for her.   " Sire, I thought to find her here ;
she arose ere I did.   Is she not come yet ? "

Quoth he : " She holds me too lightly ! "

---

[1] Containing the water-supply.

He called his chamberlain, and bade him go in all haste to know why she came not as she was wont to do.

And the man went into her chamber, and found two in her bed in each other's arms, neb [1] to neb and mouth to mouth. . . . Soon must they awaken to sorrow !

He returned anon to the tower, and told his master what he had seen ; and the emir bade bring his sword, for he would know more of this thing.

Forth he strode angerly, he and his chamberlain, and came where they two lay with sleep still heavy on their eyes.

He bade withdraw the clothes a little, and perceived that one was a maid, the other a man ; and he quaked for anguish where he stood, and had it in his mind to kill them. But yet he thought, ere he did so, to learn from them what they were.

Presently the children awoke, and saw the emir walking there with his drawn sword over them ; and sorely they were frightened, as they might well have been !

" Tell me," quoth he, " good friend, what made thee so bold as to come into my tower and lie with this maid ? To a cruel ending wert thou born ; thou shalt suffer death for this ! "

Then said Floris to Blancheflour : " There is no help but that we die ! "

Together they cried him mercy, that he spare their

[1] Nose ; properly speaking, bill or beak, as of a bird.

lives ; but he sent for his baronage to pass judgment upon
them, bade them arise and dress, and after, had them fast
bound and cast into prison.

Now came all the barons to the emir's fair palace until
it was full of earls and dukes. He stood up among them
all, in semblance well stern, and said: "Honourable lords,
ye have heard tell of Blancheflour whom I bought for
seven times her weight in gold, thinking, without doubt, to
have her for my queen. I myself came to her bedside,
and found her with a stripling! Thereupon I fell into
such hate that I thought to have killed them both ;
but although I was mad with rage, I restrained myself.
Now ye have heard the case, avenge me in your judgment ! "

Then said a king of that land : " We have understood
the affront put upon thee, but ere we deem them to death,
we must hear the children speak, and learn what they
will say, and if they will allege aught in their defence.
Else were it not right judgment, without answer to the
charge."

But the King of Nubia [1] said : " Sire, it shall not be so.
It is right enough that felons caught in the act should
suffer judgment without charge or answer."

To this all agreed, and bore witness to its truth. So the
children were brought forth to the fire that was made for
their burning ; weeping bitterly, they were led between

[1] This suggests Babylon in Egypt, Cairo.

two sergeants to their death. Sorrowful as they were, each grieved most for the other's woe.

Said Floris to Blancheflour : " There is no help but we must die, yet mine is the guilt, and it is unmeet that thou suffer death for me ! If Nature would allow, I ought to die twice, once for thee and once for me, for had I never come into this tower, thou mightest still be dwelling there in joy ! "

He drew forth the splendid ring that his mother had given him when he went away.

" Have this ring, my sweetheart. Thou mayst not die while it is thine ! "

He held it out and gave it to Blancheflour, but she said : " The fault is mine for the woe of us both ; and this ring shall never save me, for I will not see thee die ! "

Then would she have given it back to him, but in no wise would he take it. He thrust it upon her, and she flung it to the ground, where a duke saw it, and was pleased to stoop and pick it up.

Thus these children came weeping to the fire that was to be their doom ; and they were brought before all the people, heavy with sorrow. There was no stern man looked upon them but that he would fain have withdrawn the judgment, and have bought them off with much goods, had he dared to speak, for Floris was so fair a youngling, and Blancheflour so sweet a maid that even in their sorrow they were more beautiful than be the men and women nowadays in their times of most joy.

The emir was so wild with wrath that he would not withdraw his intent, but bade fast bind the children and cast them into the fire. But when the duke that had found the ring came to him and whispered, and showed him what he knew of them, he let them be called that he might speak with them, and ask Floris his name ; and anon he was told.

" Sire," said Floris, " I entreat thee not to kill that maid, for of all this guilt I am to blame ! I ought to die, and she go quit and clear ! "

Quoth Blancheflour : " Nay, kill me, and let Floris live ! "

Quoth the emir : " As I breathe, ye shall die both to-gether ! I will avenge myself ; and ye shall never go or speak more ! "

Thereupon he drew his sword out of its sheath to slay them both. Blancheflour offered her neck, but Floris thrust her away : " I am a man ; I shall go first ! Thou shalt not take death in my stead ! "

Then Floris bent his neck, but Blancheflour dragged him aside ; for neither could endure it that the other should die first.

All that saw this made dole, and the emir, wroth as he was, changed his cheer.[1] In that each would die for the

[1] Expression.

other, and he saw so many weeping all about him, and in that he loved that maid so dearly, he himself turned away for tears. His sword fell from his hand to the ground, for he could hold it no longer.

Then the duke that had found the ring sought to speak with them, and in this he sped so well that he saved them both from death.

" Sir emir," he said, " it is little to thine honour to kill these fair children ! It were better that Floris tell thee how he came into thy tower. When thou knowest his device, the more easily mayst thou deal with others."

All that heard these words besought him to grant this ; whereupon he bade Floris tell by what means he came in to Blancheflour, and who counselled and helped him to that end.

" That," quoth he, " will I never say, for anything thou canst do to me, unless thou forgive them that taught me the device ; else shall it never be told ! "

And all prayed for this too, which the emir presently granted.

Now hath he told them, beginning and end, how Blancheflour was sold away from him, and how he was a king's son of Spain, who for her love came hither to find some device whereby he might win her back, and how by his cup and other fee the porter became his man, and how he was carried within in a basket—and at this all the others laughed. Then he fell at the emir's feet, and prayed that

he might keep his sweetheart.   And the emir forgave them
both his wrath, and delivered Blancheflour to Floris ;
whereupon all his barons thanked him.

And afterwards, the emir—blessings on him !—set the
child by his side, and said he should be first of all his
meiny, and made him stand up and be dubbed knight.
And both the children in their joy fell together to kiss
his feet.

He had them brought to church and spoused with a
gold ring ; and by Blancheflour's counsel, Claris he fetched
down from the tower and made his queen.

The feast was gay enough, for there was all the glee that
might be ever at any bridal.

It was not long thereafter that a messenger came to
Floris with word that his father was dead ; and all the
baronage counselled him to wend home and take over his
kingdom.   He said farewell to the emir, who entreated him,
saying : "If thou dost by my counsel, remain with me, nor
go home, for I will give thee a kingdom as long and as
broad as ever thy father could render to thee ! "

But Floris would not at any price, for he had liefer be
with his kin.   He bade the emir good-day, and thanked
fair Claris and gave her twenty pounds of red gold, and to
Dayre for his good counsel he gave twenty pounds, and to
all that ever did well by him, he made it worth their while.
He commended them all to God Our Lord, and went
home when he might, and was crowned king ; and his

sweet wife was made queen.   He received Christendom at a priest's hand, and ever thanked God for all His mercy.

> *Now are they dead indeed—*
> *Christ of heaven our souls lead !*
> *Now this tale is brought to end*
> *Of Floris and his little friend,*
> *How they were blissful after woe ;*
> *God grant that us may happen so,*
> *That we may love Him all so well,*
> *That we may go to heaven to dwell !*
>   *Amen.*

SIR ORFEO [1]

> *Often we read and in writing find,*
> *And likewise clerks put us in mind,*
> *Of lays [2] that be made for harping,*
> *Of many a strange and ferly thing :*
> *Some be of weal and some of woe,*
> *And some of joy and mirth also,*
> *Some of treachery, some of guile,*
> *And some of haps that fell erewhile,*
> *Some of jest and ribaldry,*
> *And some there be of the Faërie,*

[1] Orpheus.   See note.   [2] See note.

Of all things that men may see,
But most of love, forsooth, they be.
All those lays were found and written
First, and spread abroad in Britain,
Of old adventures, bygone days,
Whereof the Britons made these lays.
When they might hear anywhere
Of adventures that there were,
They took their harps with glee and game,[1]
To make these lays, and gave them name.
Of old haps that once befell,
Some, not all, I can you tell.
Hearken, lordings that be true,
And I will speak of Orfeo.

HE was a king, stalwart and bold, courteous and free of
his gifts. His father came of the race of King Pluto, and
his mother of King Juno, who were sometime held as gods
for the adventures they did and told.

Now Orfeo loved most of anything glee of the harp ;
and every good harper was certain to have much honour at
his hands. He himself loved playing, and so laid his keen
wits to it and learned, that in all the world was no better
harper. There was never a man born who sat by him and
listened to his playing but thought himself in one of the
joys of Paradise, such was the melody of his music.

[1] Music and mirth.

I.

He dwelled in Traciens,[1] a city of noble defence, with his
gentle queen, Heurodis,[2] the fairest lady of that time, and
full of love and goodness. Of her beauty no man could
tell.

Now it chanced that in the beginning of May, when the
days are merry and hot, and winter rains are done, when
every field is full of flowers, and blossoms hang on every
bough, and the earth over all waxeth gay enough, this
Queen Heurodis, taking two of her fair maidens, went
early in the morning into an orchard, to see the flowers
spring up and grow, and to hear the birds singing.

They sat them down all three together under a fair imp-
tree ;[3] and presently the fair queen fell asleep on the
grass. Her maidens durst not awaken her, but let her lie
and take her rest ; and so she slept through undern [4] until
the afternoon.

But as soon as she awoke, she cried out and made a great
moaning, and twisted her hands and feet, and scratched
her face until it bled, and tore her rich robe, so clearly out
of her wits that the maids by her side durst stay with her no
longer, but ran to the palace straightway and told knight
and squire that the queen would away, and bade them go
and restrain her.

Knights ran and ladies also, sixty and more damsels

[1] Thrace. See note.   [2] Eurydice.
[3] A grafted tree. See note.
[4] Nine to twelve A.M. See note.

together ; so came to the queen in the orchard, took her up in their arms, carried her to her bed, and there held her safe, though ever she went on crying, and would be up and away.

When Orfeo heard these tidings, he was more grieved than ever before in his life, and came with ten knights into the queen's chamber, and beheld her, and said with great pity :

" O dear life, what ails thee ? Thou hast ever been so still, and now dost greet [1] with shrill crying ! And thy fair body is all torn with thy nails, thy once rosy face is as wan as thou wert dead, and thy small fingers are all pale and bleeding ! Alas, thy lovesome een stare as a man's on his foe ! Ah, lady, have pity ! Let be this rueful crying, and tell me what aileth thee, and how and in what wise I may thee help ! "

Then she lay still at last, and fell into swift weeping, and said to the king : " Alas, my lord, Sir Orfeo, since we were first married, never once have we been wroth with each other, but ever I have loved thee as my life, and so thou me ; but now we must part—do thy best, still must I go ! "

" Alas ! " quoth he, " I am forlorn ! Whither wilt thou go, and to whom ? Where thou goest, I will with thee, and where I go, thou shalt ! "

" Nay, nay, sir, that may not be ! I will tell thee how

[1] Weep.

it is. This underntide, as I lay asleep in our orchard, there appeared to me two fair armed knights who bade me come at once and speak with their lord and king; and when I answered with bold words that I neither durst nor would, they pricked away as fast as they might spur, and quickly returned with him. He was followed by an hundred men and more, and an hundred damsels all on snow-white steeds, in garments white as milk. Never in my life have I seen such beautiful creatures!

"The king had on his head a crown not of silver or of red gold, but of a single precious gem that shone like the sun. As soon as he was come to me, he caught me up, whether I would or no, and set me on a palfrey by his side, and took me to his splendid palace. Castles he showed me, and towers, rivers, forests, and flowery glades, and all his rich steadings; and at last he brought me home again to our own orchard, and said to me after: 'Look, dame, that thou be to-morrow here under this imp-tree; and then thou shalt come to dwell with us for ever. If thou makest any hindrance, thou shalt be fetched, wheresoever thou art, and all thy limbs so torn that nothing shall avail thee, and even in that state we shall bear thee away with us!'"

When Orfeo heard this, he cried: "Alas, alas! I would rather lose my life than thee, my wife and queen!"

He asked counsel of all his men, but none could help him.

On the morrow, when undern was come, he took his

weapons, and with well ten hundred knights armed stout and grim, he went with the queen right unto that imp-tree. They kept guard on every side, and said that they would stay there and die ere the queen should be taken from them. But yet from full in the midst of them all she was snatched away by the fairies, and men wist never where she was gone.

Then was there bitter weeping and woe. The king went into his chamber and swooned on the stones, and made such dole and such moan that his life was near spent, and there was no help for him. Soon he called together his barons, earls, and other lords of renown, and when they were all come, he said : " Lords, in your presence, I ordain my high steward to govern all my kingdom in my stead, and to keep my lands withal, for now that I have lost my queen, the fairest lady ever born, never again will I look upon any woman ! I shall go into the wilderness, and dwell henceforth with the wild beasts in the hoary woods. And when ye know that my life is spent, then make a parliament and choose you a new king ; so do your best with all that is mine."

Then was there weeping in the hall, and great outcry among young and old, who could scarce find a word to their tongues for sorrow. But they all kneeled down together, and prayed him, if it were his will, not to leave them.

" Away ! " he said. " It shall be so."

So he forsook his kingdom, and taking with him nor
kirtle, nor hood, nor shirt nor other goods, but only a
palmer's cloak, and his harp, he passed barefoot and alone
from the gates ; for no man would he allow to go with
him.

Ah, but there was weeping and woe, when he that had
been their crownèd king went thus poorly out of town !

Through wood he passed, and over heath into the
wilderness, and found nowhere comfort, but ever lived in
great malease. He that had once worn rich grey fur and
slept in a bed of purple pall, now lay on the hard heath
with leaves and grass for his covering. He that had once
owned castles, towers, rivers, forests and flowery glades,
now even in frost and snow must make his bed on the moss.
He that had once seen knights of prowess kneeling before
him, and ladies as well, now finds naught to his liking
among the wild serpent-kind. He that once had plenty of
meat and drink and all things dainty, now must daily grub
and dig to find his fill of roots. In summer, he lived upon
wild fruits and berries but little good ; in winter, he could
find nothing but roots and grasses and bark. So he continued till his body was shrunken for misease, and he was
all a-cough, and his beard, black and shaggy, was grown
to his girdle. Lord, who may tell what sorrow this king
suffered for ten years and more !

His harp, wherein was all his joy, he hid in a hollow tree ;
and when the weather was clear and bright, he took it to

"All the wild beasts.........gathered round him for delight."

him and played at his own will. The sound of his harping shrilled throughout the woods, so that all the wild beasts that were there gathered round him for delight; and all the birds that were there came and sat on every briar to hear his sweet playing, so much melody was therein. But as soon as he ceased to harp no beast would stay near him.

Often in the hot underntide, he saw the King of Faërie with his rout come hunting all about him with dun [1] cries and horn-blowings, and the barking of hounds. But they never took any beast, and never might he know whither they went.

At other times, he would see, as a great host, fully armed knights, well turned ten hundred, with fierce, bold faces, and with many banners displayed, and each knight holding a drawn sword; but he wist never where they went.

And at other times he saw other things, knights and ladies come a-dancing, in quaint attire disguised, with quaint steps and soft. And they had with them tabours [2] and trumpets, and all manner minstrelsy.

And on a day he saw beside him sixty ladies on horseback, as gentle and jolly [3] as birds on a bough; and there was no man among them. And each bore a falcon on her hand, and so they went a-hawking by the river, and found good haunts of game—mallard and heron and cormorant.

---

[1] Literally, *dull of colour;* here, *faint of sound.*
[2] Drums.   [3] French *joli*, pretty.

As the water-fowl arose, each falcon bore him well and seized his prey.

When Orfeo saw that he laughed. " I' faith ! " quoth he, " I will thither, in God's name ! That is a fair sport, and I was ever wont to see such work."

He rose and went up to one of the ladies, and beheld by all marks that it was his own queen, Heurodis. Yearningly he gazed on her and she on him ; but neither spoke a word to other.

Tears fell from her een when she saw him so poor that had been once so rich and high ; but when the other ladies beheld him, they made her ride away, so that she might dwell with him no longer.

" Alas ! " he cried. " Now woe is me ! Why will not death slay me ? Alas, poor wretch, that I may not die after this sight ! Alas, my life endures too long, when I may not speak with my queen, nor she with me, one word! Why will not my heart break ? *Parfay*," quoth he, " tide what may betide, I will go the same way that these ladies have taken ! I reck not of life or death ! "

Thus saying, he put on his palmer's cloak, and hung his harp on his back ; and, having good will to go, he spared for neither stub nor stone. The ladies rode into a rock,[1] and he followed after without delay ; and when he had gone three miles or more in the rock, he came to a fair country, as bright as the sun on a summer's day, smooth and level,

[1] See note.

and all green, without sign of hill or dale.   In the midst of
the land he saw a castle, rich and royal and wondrous high.
All the outermost wall was clear and shone like crystal,
and an hundred towers were set about it of quaint fashion
and stoutly embattled ; and the buttresses rising above
the dyke were of red gold richly arched.   The great hall
within was adorned with divers animals ; and there were
wide dwellings all of precious stones.   Even the worst
pillar there was made of burnished gold.

All that land was ever in light, for when dark evening
came the rich stones reflected rays as bright as the noonday sun.[1]   No man might tell or even think of all the
splendid work there wrought ; and by all marks it seemed
to be the proud court of Paradise.

At this castle the ladies dismounted, and Orfeo, following eagerly, knocked at the gate ; whereupon the porter
was ready, and asked what he would have.

" *Parfay*," quoth he, " lo ! I am a minstrel come to comfort your lord with my music, if it be his sweet will."

The porter undid the gate anon, and let him into the
castle.   He looked about, and saw lying there within the
wall a crowd of folk that had been brought thither, and
were thought to be dead but were not.[1]   Some were headless, others without arms, some had wounds through the
body, some lay mad and bound, some sat armed on horseback, some had been strangled as they ate, some had been

[1] See note.

drowned and others all shrivelled up by fire. Wives lay there in childbed, some dead and some raving mad ; and wonder many lay there right as they were taken by the fairies from the world, while they slept at underntide. Among them he saw his own wife, Heurodis, asleep under an imp-tree, for he knew her by her clothes.

When he had beheld all these marvels, he went to the king's hall wherein stood a splendid canopy, under which sat the king and his fair, sweet queen. Their crowns and their garments shone so dazzling bright that he could scarce bear to look at them.

When he had seen all these things, he kneeled before the king and said : " O lord, if it be thy will, thou shalt hear my minstrelsy."

" What man art thou ? " answered the king. " I know that none of my people have sent for thee ; and never since I first reigned here, have I found any man so foolhardy that he durst come hither to us unless I sent for him."

" Lord," answered Orfeo, " trow ye, I am but a poor minstrel ; and, sir, it is the manner of us to proffer our music in many a lord's house where we be unwelcome." [1]

He sat down before the king, and as he well could, took and tuned his merry-sounding harp. And after, he drew forth such blissful notes that all the folk in the palace came to listen to him and lay down at his feet, so dulcet they found his melody.

[1] See note.

The king sat full still, and gladly hearkened to the music that so enchanted him and his queen ; and when Orfeo came to an end, he said : " Minstrel, meliketh well thy glee ! Ask of me whatso thou wilt. Speak now and try thy power, and I will pay thee right royally for thy music ! "

" Sir," answered Orfeo, " I beseech thee to give me that lady bright of face who sleeps beneath the imptree."

" Nay," quoth the king, " that will I not ! A sorry couple ye would make, for thou art lean and rough and black, and she is most lovesome. It were a loathly thing to see her in thy company ! "

" O sir," cried Orfeo, " gentle king ! Yet were it a thing more loathly to hear a lie fall from thy lips ! So, sir, as thou saidst even now, that what I asked for I should have, thou must needs keep thy word ! "

" Since that is so," said the king, " take her by the hand and depart. I wish you joy of her ! "

Orfeo kneeled down and thanked him with all his heart. Then holding his wife by the hand, he passed quickly out of that place, and away from that people, by the same way that he had come.

So long they journeyed till they arrived at Traciens, his own city ; but at first he went no further than the town's end. No man knew that it was he, and as a poor minstrel he with his wife took lodging with a beggar but narrowly housed. There he asked tidings of his land, and who held the kingdom. The beggar in his cot told him every deal, how the queen had been stolen away by fairies ten years before, and how the king had gone into exile, no man knew where, and how the steward governed the land, and many other things.

On the morrow at noontide, leaving his wife in that place, and borrowing the beggar's clothes, he took his harp on his back and went into the city, so that men might behold him. And earls and bold barons, burgesses and ladies, ran to see.

" Lo," they said, " such a man ! How long is his hair ! And look, his beard hangeth to his knee ! Like a withered tree, he is all shrunken ! "

As he passed along the street, he met his steward, and cried aloud : " Sir steward, mercy ! I am a harper of heathendom [1]—help me now in my distress ! "

" Come with me," answered the steward. " In all that I have thou shalt share, for every good harper is welcome to me for love of my lord, Sir Orfeo ! "

In the hall the steward sat with the other barons at meat ; and there were trumpeters and tabourers and many harpers and fiddlers. While they were all making melody, Orfeo held him still and hearkened ; and when all were quiet, he took his harp and tuned it shrill, and played the sweetest notes that ever man heard. All the people loved

[1] See note.

well his music, and the steward looked, and straightway he knew that harp.

" Minstrel," he said, " as thou hopest to thrive, how didst thou obtain this harp ? I prithee, tell me."

" Lord," quoth he, " as I went through a wilderness in a strange land, I found in a hollow a man torn to pieces by lions, and wolves gnawing him with their sharp teeth. It is well ten years ago."

" Oh," cried the steward, " now woe is me ! That was my lord, Sir Orfeo. Alas, wretch, what shall I do who have lost such a lord ? Away that ever I was born ! Alas, that such scant grace was his, and that he was fore-doomed to such a vile death ! "

With this he fell a-swooning to the ground ; and the barons raised him up, and told him how it is that there is no help for a man's death.

Thereupon King Orfeo knew well that his steward was a true man and loved him as well as he deserved, and stand-ing up, he spake as follows : " Lo, now, sir steward, hearken to this thing. If I were King Orfeo and had suffered bitterly in the wilderness, and had won my queen away out of Fairyland, and had brought my sweet lady right here to the town's end and left her there with a beggar, and were myself come hither to assay thy good will, and had found thee thus true, surely thou shouldst never rue it, but for love of this love of thine, I should make thee king after my day ; but if thou hadst been glad of my death, thou shouldst straightway have been driven into exile ! "

Then all that sat there understood that it was King Orfeo himself. And the steward knew him well, and flung over the boards,[1] and fell down at his feet, and so did all the other lords, and said at once : " Ye be our lord, sir, and our king ! "

They rejoiced that he was still alive, and anon led him to his chamber, and bathed him, and shaved his beard, and attired him fittingly as a king.

Then in a great procession, and with all manner minstrelsy—Lord, what melody was there !—they brought the queen into the town. And all those that saw the king and queen safe and sound, wept for joy.

Now is King Orfeo crowned anew, and also his dame, Queen Heurodis. They lived long after, and when their time was past, the steward was king.

And presently harpers in Britain heard of this marvel, and made it into a lay of good liking, and named it after King Orfeo. It is a pleasant lay and sweet of note.

Thus came King Orfeo out of his care ;
God grant us all as well to fare !

[1] Probably, on trestles.

LAY OF THE ASH

WE read often, and clerks know well, lays that be made for the harp of ferly things, some of war and woe, and some of joy and mirth, some of treachery and guile and adventures that befell long ago, some of jests and ribaldry, and many of faërie and all things that men meet in their lives, but chiefly, indeed, of love. These lays were made in Britain in olden times; for whenever a king heard of any marvel he took his harp and made a lay thereof, and gave it name.

Of these adventures I can tell some, but not all; and I know the story of *Le Freine*, which was a strange chance that befell in Britain. In English, the name means *Ash*, and the tale is a fair ensample of olden days.

In the West Country dwelled two men, alike rich and just-dealing, each with his wedded wife.

Now the one lady became with child and in due course was delivered; whereupon the knight thanked Almighty God, and called a messenger and bade him: "Haste thee to my neighbour with my greetings, and pray that he come to me and stand sponsor."

Accordingly, the messenger went on his way, and found the knight at meat in the hall, and greeted him fair, also his lady and his household. Then he kneeled down and bespake the lord: "He bids thee come and for his love be sponsor."

" Is his lady safely unbound ? "

" Yea, sir, God be thanked the while ! "

" And whether a maid-child or a knave ? "

" Two sons, sir—God keep them ! "

Thereupon the knight was glad, and thanked God heartily, and granted the messenger's errand, and gave him a palfrey for his tidings.

But the lady of the house was a proud and envious dame, full of falsehood and mockery, touchy and scornful,[1] and bitterly jealous of any other woman ; and she spake these slanderous words : " I wonder, messenger, who gave thy lord counsel to send about and tell his shame in every place ; for if his wife hath had two children, well may folk know thereby that two men have lain in her bower, and that is dishonour to them both ! "[2]

The messenger was sore ashamed ; and the knight himself was deeply vexed, and rebuked his lady for speaking such slander of any woman. And all the women who heard her cursed her, and besought God in heaven for His Seven Holy Names' sake that if ever she had child, a worse adventure might come upon her.

Soon after, it fell out that she herself was with child, and when God willed she was unbound and safely delivered.

But when she knew that she had two maid-children, she

[1] The text is picturesque :

> " Hokerfulliche missegging,
> Squeymous and eke scorning."

[2] See note.

was in deep trouble. "Alas," she cried, "for this evil hap! I have given mine own doom! Evil betides a woman who speaks ill of another. I judged my neighbour falsely, and this same foul chance hath fallen on me! Alas," she said, "that I was born! I am forlorn without end![1] Either I must say that two men have lain by me, or that I have slandered my neighbour's wife, or I must—God forbid!—help to slay mine own child! One of these three evils I must needs say or do : if I confess that I have had a lover, I belie myself, and shall be held light and false of tongue by young and old! I had best take my chance —kill the child, and do penance after!"

She called the nurse to her and said : "Make away with this babe, and say wherever thou goest, that I had but the one, and no more."

The nurse answered that she neither could nor would do such a thing.

[Now[2] the lady had a noble maiden who had been brought up there and fostered for many a year ; and she beheld her mistress with this sorry cheer, weeping and sighing and crying out "Alas!" and thought to help her in her plight, and said : "Not for anything would I grieve thus! I will carry one of the children away, and leave it at a convent ; and so shalt thou suffer no shame. And may whoso findeth the little one, keep it for God's love and Our Lady's sake!"]

[1] Lost for ever.
[2] A gap in the MS. Supplied from the French.

I.

To this the dame agreed, and straightway wished that it were done. She took a rich mantle that her lord had brought from Constantine,[1] and lapped the little maid therein, and took a ring of fine gold which she knit about its right arm with a silken lace, so that whoever found the babe might know it came of noble kind.

At eventide, the maiden took the child and stole away. All the winter-long night she passed over a wild heath,[2] and through field and forest. The weather was clear and the moon shone. Presently, as she waxed weary, she came to a wood-side, and there rested a while.

But soon after, she heard cocks crowing and dogs barking, and going towards the sounds she beheld walls and houses a many, and a church with a fair high steeple. There was neither street nor town, but only a convent, the home of an order of nuns pledged to serve God, day and night.

The maid tarried no longer, but hastened to the church door, and there kneeled, and weeping said her orison : " O Lord Jesus Christ, Thou who hearest the prayers of sinful man, accept this gift, and help this blessed innocent to be christened, for love of Mary, Thy Mother ! "

She looked up, and saw close by a fair, tall ash-tree, many-branched and hollow of trunk, as they so often are. Therein she laid the child out of the cold, all happed [3]

---

[1] Constantinople. In the Middle Ages, its origin was explained as *Constantine the noble.*

[2] See note.

[3] Wrapped.

as it was in the fur ; and with all her heart she blessed it.

As it began to dawn, with the birds up and singing on the branches, and acre-men going to the plough, the maiden returned again by the way she had come.

Presently the abbey-porter bestirred him, and did his office in the close : he rang the bell, lit the tapers, laid forth the books, and had all things in readiness. As he undid the church door, he saw at once the fur lying in the tree. He thought that thieves might have stolen it somewhere, and then fled and left it behind them ; so he hastened thither, and unfolded it, and found the maid-child within. He took it up in his two hands, and thanked Christ for His sending.

Anon he brought it home to his house and gave it to his daughter, bidding her cherish it as she could, for she had her own babe at the breast and knew of such matters. She offered it milk, and it would none, being nigh dead of the cold. But after, she lighted a fire and warmed it well, and took it to her bosom, and presently laid it to sleep comfortably.

Now when Mass was done, the porter went to the abbess, and said : " Madam, what counsel have ye for this thing ? To-day right in the morning, soon after prime, I found a little maid-child in the hollow ash-tree, with a fur wrapped about her and a ring of gold tied to her arm ; and how she came there I know not."

At this the abbess wondered, and said : " Go at once and fetch her hither, I pray thee. She is welcome to God and to me ; and I will do for her what I can, and say that she is my kinswoman."

Thereupon the porter fetched the child, together with the mantle and the ring. And the abbess sent for a priest to christen her at the font-stone. And because she was found in an ash-tree, she was called *Freine*, for *Freine* means *ash* in the language of Britain.[1]

This Freine throve from year to year, and men supposed that she was niece to the abbess, who gave her teaching and protection. By the time that she was twelve years old, she was the fairest maid in all England ; and being then of an age to understand, she asked the abbess who were her kins-folk, father and mother, sister or brother. The abbess would not deny her, but revealed how she was found, and gave her the mantle and the ring, bidding her cherish them. And so she did as long as she lived.

Now in that country lived a rich knight, lord of many lands, proud, young and gay, and still unwedded. He was a strong man, of great renown ; and his name was Sir Guroun. Hearing this maiden so praised, he said that he would see her ; and forthwith made him ready and rode thither gaily, bidding his man give out that he was on his way to a tournament.

The abbess and all the nuns greeted him fair in the

---

[1] It is really French, not Welsh or Breton.

guest-hall ; and the damsel Freine, so sweet and gracious of her words, spoke with him courteously, as she well could. And so he set before himself her beauty, her grace, her lovesome eyes and her fair countenance, that he began straightway to love her, and to cast about in his mind how he might have her for his mistress.   He thought : " If I come here more than I have done, the abbess will suspect guile, and will shortly send her away."   So he devised another plan, which was to be a brother of that religion. " Madam," he said to the abbess, " I admire godliness so greatly that I would give both lands and rents to become a lay brother ; and ye shall fare ever the better for granting me entertainment."   With a few words they were at one, and he made ready to depart, and rode away.

After that he came often, both day and night, to speak with that sweet maiden, so that in the end, by reason of his fair promises and his flattery, she granted him his will.

" Sweetheart," he said, " thou must leave the abbess, thine aunt, and come with me, for I am rich and of great power.   Thou shalt find it better there than here ! "

The maiden trusted him and consented, and stole away, taking naught with her save her mantle and her ring. When the abbess found that Freine was gone, she mourned her loss heavily and bemoaned the maiden's fate, but gained nothing thereby.

Now Freine lived with the knight in his castle long time, and all his household loved her well.   She cared for

rich and poor alike, and lived right as though she had
been his wedded wife.

But after a time, his knights came and spoke with him,
and Holy Church commanded him to forsake his mistress
and marry some lord's daughter.   They said it were more
seemly to get an heir in wedlock than to lead this life with
one of whose kindred he knew nothing, and they added
further : " Here beside is a knight whose lovely daughter
shall have his heritage ; take her to wife."   And he was
right loth to do so, but at last consented.

The deed was made ready, and they were troth-plight.
Alas, that he knew not ere the covenant was signed that
she and his mistress were twin-sisters !   Of one father and
mother were they born, but none knew this save God
alone.

The new bride, whose name was Le Codre,[1] was arrayed
and brought home to the lord's hall.   Her father and
mother and many more came with her, and also the bishop
of that land to do the spousing.[2]

[The marriage feast was held with great splendour and
rejoicing.   All the while, Freine was in the chamber and
gave no sign of grief or of anger.   Sweetly and deftly she
served the lady, so that all the guests held her demeanour in
great marvel.   Her own mother, watching, commended

---

[1] Hazel.

[2] Here the MS. breaks off.   The tale is finished from the
version of Marie de France, not from Weber's reconstruction.

her in secret, and loved her, and thought that if she had known what manner of woman this was, not for her own daughter's sake would she have parted her from her lord.

At night the damsel went to prepare the marriage-bed ; but she thought the coverlet poor, ill-beseeming so fair a bride, and she ran quickly to her own coffer and took out her own rich mantle to lay upon the bed, in honour of her lord.

And presently the bride and her mother came into the room, and the dame beheld that mantle, which was like none other that she had seen, save only the one in which she had wrapped the little daughter that she had put away. All her heart trembled as she sent for the chamberlain and asked him whose it was.

" Lady," he said, " know that the damsel here hath brought it to lay upon the bed because it seemed to her ill set out.   It is her own, I trow."

Then the lady sent for her, and she came with humble cheer.

" Dear child," said the lady, " hide nothing from me. Where got you this mantle of fair silk ?   Who gave it you ? Tell me the truth."

" Madam," she said, " the abbess, mine aunt, who fostered me, gave it me, bidding me keep it well, for, together with a ring, it was left with me by those who put me away to be nurtured."

" Dear, may I see the ring ? "

" Yes, madam, right willingly."

And thereupon the lady studied it long, knowing it as well as she knew the mantle ; and when she perceived that Freine was her daughter, she could hide it no further, but said : " Dear heart, thou art my child ! "

For sheer pity she swooned ; but presently she recovered and sent for her husband.   And when he came thither, greatly astonished, she kneeled before him and entreated forgiveness.

And when he had granted this, though he knew not what she meant, she said : " My lord, long ago I foolishly slandered a neighbour of mine because of her twin-children.   And all the while I was speaking to mine own hurt, for afterwards, of a truth, I had twin-daughters. But the one child I put away and had left at a convent, and with her your silk mantle and the ring that ye gave me as a love-token.   But now I may hide it no more, for here I have found our dear daughter whom through my folly I had lost !   This is she, this fair and modest damsel whom the knight loved that hath wedded her sister."

Said the baron : " Never in my life before have I been so glad ! "

And when he had kissed his daughter, he went for the archbishop and the young knight and brought them thither, repeating to them all that tale.   And when Guroun heard this, he rejoiced as never before in all his days.

On the morrow, the marriage with Le Codre was undone ; and the young knight was married to her sister, to
whom their father gave a share in his heritage.

Then they made a feast so splendid that even a rich man
might well grudge what was spent upon it. And presently
Le Codre returned with her parents to their domain, and
soon after was well bestowed in marriage.

When this adventure became known, it was made into a
lay, and for the lady's sake called *Lai le Freine*.]

LAUNFAL MILES [1]

IN the brave days of King Arthur, who held England in
good laws, there befell a wondrous adventure, whereof
was made a lay that was called *Launfal*, and is yet—will
ye hearken to it ?

For some time King Arthur sojourned at Carlisle [1] with
great mirth and disport, he and his goodly knights of the
Round Table,[1] Sir Percival and Sir Gawayn, Sir Gaheris
and Sir Agravayne, and Lancelot du Lake, Sir Kay and Sir
Iwayn, a good fighting-man to undertake battles, King
Ban-Booght and King Bos of wide fame, Sir Galafre, and
Sir Launfal of whom is this tale.

For many a year he had dwelled a bachelor at Arthur's

[1] See note.

court, and had scattered abroad largess of gold and silver and rich apparel, alike to squire and knight. And in that his bounty was greatest of all the Round Table, he was made king's steward, and so continued for ten years in that place.

In the tenth year it befell that Merlin,[1] Arthur's counsellor, gave him rede[2] to go into Ireland to fetch him thence the bright lady Guinevere, the comely daughter of King Ryence in that land. So he did, and brought her home to wife; but she was not liked of Sir Launfal and other honourable knights, her fame being that she favoured gallants in secret from her lord.

Upon a Whitsunday they were wedded, before princes of high degree. No man could ever tell in his tale what folk were at that bridal, from countries far and wide; but none might take his place in the hall if he were less than prelate or baronet,[3] and although each was set according to his estate, the service was alike rich and splendid to all.

When these lords had feasted and the cloths were withdrawn, the butlers sent wine to them all, with glad cheer and blithe; and for the nonce the queen gave gifts of gold and silver and precious stones to show her courtesy. Brooch or ring she gave to every knight there save Launfal,

---

[1] See note.   [2] Counsel.

[3] Probably *banneret*—knight-landowner. *Baronets* were first created by James I.

to whom she gave nothing; whereby he was put to chagrin.

Now when the bridal was at an end he took leave of King Arthur, saying that a letter was come to him that his father was dead and he must to the burying.

Then said King Arthur courteously : " Launfal, if thou must depart, take with thee great spending,[1] and my sister's two sons to convey thee home."

So Launfal bade farewell to the knights of the Round Table, and went forth on his journey till he came to Caerleon,[2] to the house of the mayor of that town, who had been his servant.

There stood the mayor himself, as ye shall hear, and watched him ride up on his ambling nag, he with his two knights and other meiny ; and presently the mayor went to meet him, saying : " Sir, thou art welcome. Tell me how fares our king ? "

Then Launfal answered and said : " He fares as well as any man ; and it were great pity else ! But, Sir Mayor, truth to tell, I am parted from the king, to my sore grief ; and now need no man, above or below, honour me longer for Arthur's love. Sir Mayor, for the sake of our old acquaintance, may I sojourn with thee ? We knew each other some while, of yore."

The mayor stood and bethought him what might be his

---

[1] Money to spend.
[2] Caerleon-on-Usk, near Newport. See note.

answer, then he said : " Sir, seven knights have taken inn
here, and even now I await their coming. They are of
Little Britain." [1]

Launfal turned himself about and laughed scornfully,
and said to his knights twain : " Now ye may see of what
worth is service under a lord of small degree, and how he
may be fain of it ! "

Therewith he began to ride away, but the mayor begged
him to tarry, and spoke in this wise : " Sir, on the orchard
side is a chamber where ye may dwell with comfort and
honour, if ye will."

So Launfal presently alighted, and he and his two
knights sojourned there together ; but so savagely he made
onslaught on his goods that he fell into great debt, right in
the first year.

Thus it happened that at Pentecost, that time when the
Holy Ghost descended upon mankind, Sir Hugh and Sir
John took their leave of Sir Launfal.

" Sir," they said, " our robes are all ragged, and your
treasure is done, and we go hence in evil estate."

Then said Launfal to his noble knights : " For the love
of Almighty God, tell no man how poor I am ! " And
they answered that they would not betray him to win all
this world, and with that they left him.

They went together to Glastonbury,[2] where King
Arthur was at that time. Seeing his gentle kinsmen, he

---

[1] Brittany.   [2] See note.

came forth to meet them, all as they were, in the same
robes, now worn and ragged, in which they had gone away.

Then said the cruel Queen Guinevere: " How fares the
proud Launfal? Can he still wield his weapons? "

" Yea, madam," said the knights. " He fares as well as
any man, else God forfend!" And then they told to
King Arthur and Queen Guinevere much that was worthy
and honourable of Launfal, and said: " He loved us so
much that he would have kept us at his will evermore.
But it happened that he went a-hunting in the grey woods
on a rainy day; and so we wore our old clothes and came
away just as we were."

Now King Arthur was glad that Launfal prospered, but
the queen was sorely vexed, for with all her heart she
wished him, day and night, in pains that should grow ever
the greater.

Upon the feast of Trinity, a stately banquet was held in
Caerleon. Earls, barons, and ladies of that country, and
burgesses of the city, both young and old, came thither to
that assembly; but Launfal was not bidden, because he
was poor and men spoke little of him.

When the mayor had set off to the feast, came his
daughter to Launfal, and asked if he would dine with her
in hall that day.

" Nay, damsel," said he, " I have no heart to dine.
These three days past I have neither eaten nor drunk
because of my poverty. To-day I would have gone to

church, but lacked hosen and shoon, clean shirt and breeches, and for default of clothing might not throng in with the people—what wonder if I am sad ? But one thing, damsel, I pray thee, lend me saddle and bridle that I may ride awhile this morning in a glade outside the city, and so comfort me."

He made ready his horse, without knave or other squire ; and he rode so carelessly that his beast slipped and fell in the fen ; whereupon he was a mark of scorn to all that stood about him far and near. Again he mounted, and to make an end of mockery spurred away to the west.

The weather was hot that morning-tide, so he dismounted in the shade of a fair forest, and, folding his mantle together, sat down to rest under a tree where it liked him.

As he sat there, full sorrowful, he beheld two gentle maidens coming out of the hoar woods. Their kirtles were of Indian sendal,[1] laced small and pretty and trim— no gayer ladies might be ! Their mantles were of green velvet, embroidered featly in gold, and furred with grey *gris*.[2] Their heads were garlanded, each with a gay coronal of sixty gems and more. Their faces were as white as snow on the downs,[3] and they had brown eyes and rosy cheeks—I never saw their like ! The one bare a gold basin, the other a fine milk-white towel of good, rich silk.

---

[1] Some kind of silk.

[2] Some grey fur not clearly identified.   [3] See note.

Their kerchiefs were brightly arrayed with splendid gold thread.

Launfal sighed as they came to him over the heath; but in courteous wise he went towards them and greeted them kindly.

"God be with you, damsels," he said; and they in turn to him: "Sir knight, hail to thee! Our lady, Dame Tryamour,[1] bade thee come and speak with her, if it be thy will, nor tarry here longer."

This Launfal quickly granted the flower-white maidens with all courtesy, and went with them until they were come to a pavilion in the forest, gaily painted and of great splendour. It was wrought, forsooth, of Saracen work,[1] and the pommels[2] were all of crystal. Upon the top stood an eagle of fine burnished gold set with rich enamel; its eyes were carbuncles[3] and shone by night as brightly as the moon that sheds her rays over all. Neither Alexander the conqueror, nor King Arthur in all his glory, had ever such a jewel!

In the pavilion he found Dame Tryamour, daughter of Olyroun,[1] king of all the fairies of the Occident, far and near, and a man of much might.

There was a splendid bed covered with dark purple, seemly to look upon; and therein lay lovesomely that gentle lady who had sent for Launfal. For heat she had

---

[1] See note.   [2] Ornaments in the shape of balls.
[3] See note on *Floris and Blancheflour*, p. 179.

put down her clothes almost to her girdle ; and as she lay uncovered she was as white as a lily in May, or snow that snoweth in the winter-tide—never had he seen a damsel so debonaire. The red rose, new-blown, would have paled against her blushes ; and I do assure you that her hair shone like threads of gold. Of her attire no man could tell, nor even think of it clearly in his mind !

" Launfal," she said, " dear heart, I have left all my joy, sweeting, for love of thee ! There is no man in Christendom, neither king nor emperor, that I love so well as thee ! "

Launfal looked at that sweet flower and kissed her, and all his love went out to her. Sitting down by her side, he said : " Sweetheart, whatsoever befall, I am at thy service ! "

" Gentle knight," she said, " and kind, I know thy estate from first to last, so be not ashamed before me ! If thou wilt love me truly, and for me forsake all women, I will make thee rich. I will give thee a purse of silk and clear gold, with three fairy images thereon ; and as often as thou dost put thy hand into it, in whatsoever place thou be, thou shalt find therein a mark of gold.[1] Also, I give thee Blaunchard, my loyal steed, and Gyfre, mine own knave ; and of my arms thou shalt have a small banner with three painted ermines. In war or in tournament, no knight's blow shall hurt thee, so well shall I thee save ! "

[1] About thirteen shillings and fourpence.

" Gramercy, sweet one," answered the gentle knight.
" Nothing could please me more ! "

The damsel then arose and bade her maidens bring clear
water for her hands : and it was straightway done.

The cloth was laid, the board spread, and they went to
supper. Meat and drink they had at their will, spiced
wine, claret and rhenish—else were it great wonder !

When they had supped, and the day was gone, they
passed the night together ; and when it was the dawn of
another morrow, she bade him rise anon.

" Gentle sir knight," said she, " if thou wilt ever speak
with me in any wise, go to some secret place, and I will
come to thee as still as any stone, so that no man alive shall
see me. But of one thing I warn thee, thou must never
boast of me for any reason whatever, else hast thou lost
my love."

Then was Launfal so blithe that he could not have told
any man his joy ; and he kissed her often and enough, as
he took his leave.

Gyfre brought him his steed, and so he sprang into
the saddle and rode home to Caerleon, still in his poor
garments. In his heart he was content ; and all the
morning he held him quiet in his chamber.

There came riding through the city ten well-harnessed
men on sumpter horses, some with silver, some with gold,
some with splendid garments and bright armour, which
they brought as gifts to Sir Launfal ; and they asked
I.

where abode that knight. The young men were clad in
Indian silk, and Gyfre rode behind on the flower-white
horse, Blaunchard.

Then said a boy standing in the market-place : " How
far are all these things going ? Tell us, *par amour.*"

And Gyfre answered : " They are sent as a present to Sir
Launfal, who hath been living in great poverty."

" He is but a poor fellow," said the boy. " What man
recks of him ? He dwells at the mayor's house."

There then they dismounted, and gave the noble knight
such things as were sent him.

When the mayor saw all that richness and Sir Launfal's
great estate, he held himself in evil plight, and said : " Sir,
for charity, eat with me in hall to-day. Yesterday I had
meant that we should be at the feast together and have
joy and mirth, but erst thou wert gone."

" God reward thee, Sir Mayor," answered Launfal ;
" while I was in my poverty thou didst never bid me to
dinner, and now have I more gold and fee sent me by my
friends than belongs to thee and thine ! " And the mayor
went away for very shame.

Launfal now clad himself in purple furred with white
ermine ; and Gyfre returned in full, according to tally and
score, all that his master had borrowed beforetimes.

He held great feasts, fed fifty poor guests who were
in misfortune, bought fifty strong steeds, gave fifty rich
garments to knights and squires, rewarded fifty men of

religion, delivered fifty poor prisoners and made them quit and free, clothed fifty jesters, and did honour to many men, in countries far and near.

And at last the lords of Caerleon let cry a tournament in the town for love of Sir Launfal, and for Blaunchard his good steed, to know how he that was so well endued should prosper.

And when the day was come for which the jousting had been set, the lords of the castle rode out anon, all in a row, to the sound of trumpets. The tournament began, and every knight laid good blows on every other, alike with maces and with swords. Men might behold some steeds won and some lost, and knights wonder wroth. Never was held better tournament since the Round Table first was ordained, I dare well say.

Many a lord of Caerleon that day was overborne. The mighty constable himself would no longer abide, but rode up to Launfal and smote at him, and so Launfal in turn; and they fought with stern, grim strokes on each side until Launfal had the advantage and bore that other to the ground; and when he was down Gyfre leaped into his saddle and rode away.

When the Earl of Chester [1] saw that, he was near mad in his heart for wrath; and riding up to Sir Launfal, he smote him on his helmet so that his crest flew away— so says the French tale. But Launfal was so strong

[1] See note.

that he only dismounted, and bore the earl down to the dust.

Then a great rout of Welsh knights came about him[1]—I know not how many ; and men might see shields riven, spears split and splintered, behind and eke before. By Launfal and his steed many a knight verily was borne to the ground. So the prize of the tourney was given to Launfal that day, without oath-taking.

Afterwards he rode into Caerleon, to the mayor's house, many a lord with him ; and there he held a rich feast and splendid that lasted a fortnight. Earls and barons a many were set seemly in the hall and served royally. And every day at night came Dame Tryamour to Launfal's chamber, and none that ever were there saw her, save Gyfre and his lord.

Now there was a knight in Lombardy[1] called Sir Valentine, who had great envy of Launfal, for he had heard speak of him, that he could joust well and was a man of might. Sir Valentine himself was wonder strong, being fifteen feet tall ; and he felt all a-flame to tilt or fight with Launfal in a field between themselves. So, sitting in his hall, he called a messenger, and bade him go to Britain to the knight who was held of such prowess : " Say to him that for love of his lady, if she be gentle, courteous, free and kind, he come to tourney with me to keep his harness from rusting, and otherwise hurt his manhood."

[1] See note.

The messenger went forth at his lord's bidding. He had the wind at his will, and when he was come over the water, he took his way to Launfal, and greeted him with peaceable words, and said : " Sir ! my lord, Sir Valentine, a noble warrior and quaint of device, hath sent me to thee, and prays thee for thy lady's sake to joust with him."

Now Launfal laughed quietly, and answered that by his gentlehood, he would joust with Sir Valentine that day fortnight. And he gave the messenger for his tidings a noble courser, a ring, and a robe of striped cloth.[1]

He took leave of Tryamour—for that bright lady was even then in his chamber ; and when he kissed her, she said : " Dread thee nothing, gentle sir knight, for thou shalt overcome him on that day."

Naught would he take with him save Blaunchard, his steed, and of all his meiny, only Gyfre, his knave. Then he went on board ship with a fair wind, and crossed the salt flood to Lombardy. And when he was come over the water, he went to the city of Atalye,[2] where the jousts were to be held.

There Valentine awaited him with a great host ; but Launfal, with his little company, soon stopped his boasting ; for when he was geared with helm and spear and shield, and mounted on Blaunchard, his light-footed steed,

[1] See note.
[2] Chaucer's *Satalye*—ancient Attaleia, now Adalia or Satalia (?). But this is a seaport in Asia Minor.

the folk that beheld him in his shining armour said they
had never seen such a knight. The two then rode
together, and their spears splintered and scattered in the
field. They rode together another course, and Sir Launfal's helmet slipped off, as the tale goes. Thereupon Sir
Valentine laughed and made good sport; and Launfal
had never before been so put to shame in any fight. But
Gyfre showed that he was good at need, for unseen by any
man, he leaped on his master's horse, and ere the two
knights met again, he had set his lord's helmet on, fair and
featly. At this Launfal was glad and blithe, and thanked
Gyfre heartily for his brave deed. Then Sir Valentine
smote Launfal so that his shield fell from him; but ere it
touched the ground, Gyfre caught it up and gave it back
to his lord.[1] Joyously then Launfal rode a third time,
and as a knight of much main, smote Sir Valentine so that
both horse and man fell dead, groaning with a grisly
wound.

As soon as Valentine was slain, all the lords of Atalye
had envy of Launfal, and swore that he should die ere he
went out of Lombardy, and be hanged and drawn; but
Sir Launfal unsheathed his falchion, and in a little while
laid them down as lightly as falls the dew. And when they
were all slain, he returned to Britain with great mirth
and rejoicing.

The tidings of his exploits reached King Arthur, who

[1] See note.

anon sent him a letter that he should come to court at
St. John's Mass; [1] and since he was so given to largess,
that he should again be steward in the hall, and should
direct the great feast that would be held on that day, for
earls and barons bold, and lordings of every degree. So
he took leave of Tryamour, to go and govern the king's
feast.

There he found much mirth and state, and ladies bright
in bower, and a great company of knights. Forty days
lasted the feast right royally; and at the end of that time
the lords took leave to wend, each his own way.

After meat, Sir Gawayn, Sir Gaheris, and Agravayne
went with Sir Launfal to dance on the green beneath the
tower where the queen lay, with sixty maidens and more.
Launfal, who was loved the best of all for his largess, was
set to lead the dance; and the queen leaned forth and
watched them.

" There is Launfal dancing," she said, " that man of
bounty! I will go down to him. He is the fairest
bachelor among all the knights I see. He never had a
wife; so, tide me good or ill, I will go about to learn his
disposition, for I love him as my life!"

She took with her a company of five and sixty ladies, the
fairest she could gather; and in orderly throng they
passed down to disport them with the knights.

The queen herself went to the foremost end,[2] between

[1] June 21st.   [2] The head of the dance.

Launfal and Gawayn the courteous ; and, following her ensample, her ladies went all to take part in the dance ; and indeed it was a fair sight to see them at it, always a lady and a knight together.

When the dance grew slack, the queen took Launfal aside, and spoke in this manner : " Sir knight, of a truth I have cherished thee in my heart these seven years; and certes, I die for very love of thee, Launfal, dear friend ! "

" By God that ruleth all," he answered gently, " I will never turn traitor, night or day ! "

" Fie on thee, coward ! " then she cried. " Thou art worth no more than hanging, high and stiff ! That thou hast ever been born, or livest now, 'tis pity, for thou lovest no woman, and no woman thee ! Thou wert better forlorn ! "

At this the knight was bitterly ashamed, and could not forbear to speak, but said to the queen : " A fairer woman than thou didst ever lay eyes upon I have loved these seven years and more ! Her loathliest maiden, beyond a doubt, might better be a queen than thou at thy best ! "

Thereupon the queen was mightily wroth. She gathered her maidens, and they went back together anon, up into her tower.

There she took to her bed, sick with rage, and swore, as she hoped to thrive, so should she be avenged on Launfal that the land should ring with it in five days' time !

When King Arthur came from hunting, blithe and gay,

and went to his chamber, straightway the queen cried out
to him : " Save I be avenged I shall die !   My heart will
break in three ! [1] I spoke to Launfal in mirth, and he
besought me, to my shame, to be his mistress ! And of one
of his lemans he made this boast that the loathliest maid
she had might well be queen above me ! "

The king in great wrath swore by God that Launfal
should be slain ; and he sent doughty knights to bring
him to be hanged and drawn.

While they sought him he was gone to his chamber to
seek comfort with his love ; but she, as she had warned
him erst, was lost to him and would not come.

Then was Launfal right sorrowful. He looked in the
purse that had furnished him with spending whenever he
had need ; but it was empty, sooth to say. And Gyfre
had ridden away on Blaunchard his steed. All that he had
gained was melted like snow in the sun ; his armour that
had been flower-white was now black of hue. Then he
cried out :

" Alas, how shall I live without thee, sweetheart Tryamour ?   All my joy is done ; and, worst of all, I have lost
thee, lovesome lady ! "

Thereupon he beat his head and body, and cursed the
mouth that had uttered those foolish words ; and for trouble
and sore grief, at that time, he fell swooning to the ground.

But straightway came four knights, who bound him and

[1] See note.

led him before King Arthur ; and then was he in double woe.

" Vile and attainted traitor ! " cried the king. " Why didst thou make such boasting that thy leman's loathliest maid was fairer than my queen ? That was a foul lie ! And before, thou didst beseech her to be thy mistress, which was a misproud [1] liking ! "

With eager mood the knight answered as he stood before the king, the queen looking on : " As I am a man, I never besought her to folly ; but she said that I was naught, and that no woman loved me, or gave me her company ; and I answered her that my lady's loathliest maid was better worthy to be queen. And certes, lords, this is true ! Therefore I am ready to abide what the court shall deem."

Twelve knights [2] were set to write down all that passed. And they that took up the quest, knowing the queen's ill fame, that she had never forsaken to have lovers besides her own lord, said that it was all long of [3] the queen and not of Launfal, and that they would clear him if he could bring the lady of whom he made such boasting, and if her maidens were fairer-faced than the queen, he should be held a true man; but if he could not show his mistress, they agreed that he should be hanged like a thief. And so they proffered him to bring his sweetheart or lose his head.

---

[1] Presumptuous.   [2] Some form of trial by jury.
[3] Because of.

Then the queen spoke : " If he bring one fairer than I am, put out my two grey eyes ! "

The wager was taken in hand, and two noble knights, Sir Percival and Sir Gawayn, stood as sureties for Launfal until a certain day, which was after a twelvemonth and a fortnight ; and within this time he must show his lady.

Now the good knight Sir Launfal wrung his hands in sorrow and care, and would gladly have foregone his life and his head together ; and every man grieved that knew his evil case.

The certain day drew near, and his sureties brought him before the king, who marked him well and bade him show his lady. And he said that he was right sorrowful, but he might not do so.

Then the king commanded his barons to give judgment and condemn him to be slain ; but the Earl of Cornwall,[1] who was with them at that council, said : " We will not do so ! It were great shame to condemn that noble knight ! Therefore, lords, do by my counsel : we will lead the king another way, and Launfal shall flee out of the land."

And as the barons stood thus speaking, they saw ten lovely maidens come a-riding ; they deemed them so fair and bright as that the loathliest one might have been their own queen.

Then said Gawayn, the knight courteous : " Launfal,

[1] See note.

brother, dread thee no whit! Here comes thy gentle
lady."

But Launfal answered: "Gawayn, dear friend, verily,
not one of these is my sweetheart."

They went right to the castle, and dismounted at the
gate; and, going up to King Arthur, bade him make ready
at once a fair chamber for their lady, who was of blood
royal.

"Who is your mistress?" asked Arthur.

"Ye shall soon know," answered the maid, "for she
comes riding here."

Then the king gave command that the fairest chamber
in his palace should be prepared for her.

But straightway he sent to his barons to give judgment
on that proud traitor. Anon they answered: "Once we
have seen the bright maidens we shall not abide long."
And again, to please their lord the king, they sent a new
tale, that some condemned him while others made him
quit and clear—bold enough was their talking!

Presently, as they were about to judge him, they saw
ten other lovely maids, fairer to behold than the first
ten. They came a-riding on gay Spanish mules, with
saddles and bridles of Champagne, and reins that gleamed
brightly; and they were clothed all in attire of samite.[1]
And every man there had great desire to see their gay
weeds.

[1] A satin-like silk.

Then said Gawayn the courteous : " Launfal, here comes thy lady to bring thee release."

But Launfal answered drearily, and said : " Alas, I find her not in all that throng ! "

They rode forth on to the palace, and dismounted at the high daïs before King Arthur. After greeting the king and queen, one maid spoke these words : " Have thy hall decked, and the walls covered with rich cloths and hangings, against the coming of my lady Tryamour."

" By our Lord, the Saviour," answered the king straightway, " welcome, ye maidens sheen ! "

He commanded Lancelot du Lake to bring them, with mirth and much honour, to the same chamber wherein their sisters were.

But the queen, suspecting guile, that Launfal would soon be quit and clear through the coming of his lady, said anon to King Arthur :

" Sir, if thou wert courteous or didst love thine own honour, I should now be avenged on that traitor, who hath changed all my cheer ! Thou shouldst not spare Launfal, for thy barons but lead thee on to thine own undoing ! "

But even as she spoke, they all saw a gay damsel come riding alone on a comely white palfrey ; she was as gentle and pretty as a bird on the bough, and in all ways fair enough to dwell in any house of mortal man. She was as sweet as the briar-blossom, with grey eyes that shone with

a lovely cheer in her bright face.   She was like the red rose
on its stem, and her hair gleamed like threads of gold under
her golden crown set with dazzling gems.   Her graceful,
slender body was attired in purple silk, her mantle furred
with white ermine, turned back all pretty and fine.   Her
saddle was goodly ; the housings were all of green velvet,
painted with imagery, and bordered with nothing less
than gold bells ; and in the peaks, before and behind, were
set two brilliant stones of the Indies, while the pectoral[1] of
her palfrey, gay and strongly made, was worth the best
kingdom in Lombardy.

Her palfrey came on a soft pace that men might see her.
On her hand she bore a gerfalcon ; and by her side, as she
rode through Caerleon, ran two white greyhounds with
golden collars.

When Launfal saw that lady, at once he cried aloud to
all the folk, both young and old : " Here comes my sweet
mistress ! An she would, she might free me from my
troubles ! "

She rode forth into the hall, where was the queen with
her ladies, and also King Arthur.   Her own maidens came
to take her stirrup ; and then she doffed her mantle on the
floor, that men might see her the better, and went straight
up to the king, who gave her courteous greeting, and she
him with pleasant words.

Up stood the queen and her ladies, the better to behold

---

[1] **Trappings in front of the breast.**

her all about, and how she stood straight and comely ; and by her side they were all as dull as is the moon against the sun in daylight.

To King Arthur she said : " Sir, I come hither for one thing—to acquit the knight Launfal. Never at any time did he the folly of seeking the queen's love ; but, Sir King, she besought him to be her gallant ; and he answered her and said that his lady's loathliest maid was fairer than she."

Said the king without oath : " All may see that it is true ; ye are the fairer."

Thereupon Dame Tryamour went up to the queen, and blew upon her such a breath that she never had her sight again.

Anon the lady leaped on her palfrey, and bade them all good-day. And even then came Gyfre out of the forest with Launfal's steed, which he straightway brought up to his lord's side. Forthwith Launfal sprang to horse, and followed his mistress as, with her maidens, she returned with pride and joy the way she had come, onward through Caerleon to the beautiful isle called Olyroun.[1]

And every year, upon a certain day, men may yet see Launfal, and hear the neighing of his steed. He that is bent upon a course or two, to keep his armour from rusting, in tournament or in battle, may there tilt with Sir Launfal.

[1] Oleron, off the coast of France.

Thus was this knight of the Round Table taken into the Faërie, and after seen of no man in this land.

> *Thomas Chester made this tale*
> *Of Sir Launfal, without fail,*
>   *Good of chivalry.*
> *Jesus that is Heaven's King,*
> *Give us all His dear blessing,*
>   *And His Mother Marie !*

THE EARL OF TOULOUSE

> *Jesus Christ in Trinity,*
> *Only God and Persons Three,*
>   *Grant us well to speed,*
> *And give us grace so to do,*
> *That we may come Thy bliss unto,*
>   *On Rood as Thou didst bleed !*
> *Lief lords, I shall you tell*
> *Of a tale that sometime fell,*
>   *In a land unknown, indeed ;*
> *How a lady had great mischief,*
> *How she recovered from that grief—*
>   *I pray you, give good heed.*

THERE was once in Almayne [1] an emperor of great might called Sir Dioclysian,[2] a bold man and stout, and feared of

---

[1] Germany.   [2] Diocletian.

all christendom, so strong was he in battle. He had disherited many a man, and wickedly won their possessions by force of arms, till it befell on a day that war awakened between him and a knight called Sir Barnard, Earl of Toulouse. With him the emperor had dealt hardly, and had bereft him of three hundred pounds' worth of land ; thereupon, sore aggrieved, and himself a strong, hardy man, upon seeing how he was wronged and other men also, he prepared for battle, and, passing into the emperor's lands, began to burn and slay.

Now this emperor had to wife the fairest woman that ever lived save the Blessed Mary herself. And she was also bountiful ever in almsgiving, and as true a lady, it was well known, as she was fair. She said to the emperor : " My dear lord, I prithee, give the earl his right ! "

" Dame," he answered, " let be, for thou shalt never see the day, as long as I can ride, that he shall have his land again ! As I am a true knight, I will break his skull ! He wars fast in my country, but I shall be ready against him within a fortnight."

He sent about everywhere that men should arm them to fight the earl ; and he let cry on all sides throughout his land, far and near, in field and town, that every man who could bear weapons, sword, arbalest,[1] shield, and spear, should be ready boun.[2] And the earl, for his part,

---

[1] Strong-bow.   [2] Northern for *ready*.

I.

had forty thousand and more, with spears and brown [1] swords.

A day was set for battle, and when they met together in the field many a crown was cracked. The emperor had seven battalions, and to them he spoke sternly, saying : " As I hope to thrive, be ye now ready for to fight. Go and beat them down utterly, and spare none. Look that no man be ransomed for gold or fee, but slay them all with sword and knife ! "

For all his boasting, he failed when the earl met him manly in the field with good strokes. They upreared battle on every side, boldly riding together with shield and many a spear. They laid on like madmen, with mighty swords and axes, and made a noise full hideous. Shields and shafts were splintered, and heads were cracked through their helmets, and many a hauberk torn. The earl himself, doughty in battle, drew an axe, and slew an hundred men that day. Many a steed was pierced through, and many a bold baron lay burling [2] in his own blood. And so much blood was spilled that the field was swamped as it had been flood-time. Many a wife might, after that, sit and weep that was wont to sleep softly ; and many a bold knight, once wild and fierce, lay there dead and now worthless.

The Earl of Toulouse won the field. The emperor saw this, and fled full fast to a castle there beside, fain to

---

[1] An O. E. epithet for swords.   [2] Bubbling.

hide his head, and with him three earls. No more, forsooth, escaped that day, but all were slain or taken—it might not be otherwise. The earl followed the chase until night; and then thanked God that sits in Trinity for the grace He had shown. On the emperor's side in that battle were slain sixty thousand men, and three hundred and fifty great lords were taken, with wounds grimly wide; while the earl lost but twenty, so boldly did they fight, and such grace did God grant them that the false quarrel should come to an ill ending, in spite of all that might betide.

Now the emperor was bitterly grieved at the loss of his men and land, and sighed heavily, and swore by Him that died on the Rood, not to touch meat or drink till he should be avenged. But the empress said : " Good my lord, it is better ye should make peace for aught that I can see. By God, methinks it is a great peril to be against the right ! "

" Dame," said the emperor, " I have much dishonour, and my heart is sore ! Mine earls are slain and brought to their ending, and I am so full of care that I myself am well nigh dead of grief ! "

" Sire," said Dame Beaulybon,[1] " I rede, by St. John, that in this war of yours ye have the wrong, and he has the right; and so ye may see plainly by this and other things."

[1] Beau-li-bon, *i.e.*, beautiful and good, without regard to gender.

Thereupon he was ill-pleased, for what the lady said was true. Sighing heavily, he went away and spoke never a word more, but held him wonder still.

Let us leave now the emperor liking nor game nor glee, so mightily he grieveth, and turn again to the earl, who hath given hearty thanks to God for sending him such grace.

This Earl Barnard of Toulouse had many knights of chivalry taken in his prisons and had much good profit—as I hope to thrive, I cannot tell how much !—of their great ransoms. Chief among them all was Sir Tralabas of Turkey, a famous lord of many a town, whom the emperor cherished. It fell out one day that the earl and he went for sport along a river-side, and said the earl to Sir Tralabas :

" Tell me, sir, for God's sake, of a thing that is spread abroad, how your emperor has a wife who is the fairest woman alive. By book and bell, I swear that if she be as lovely as men say, he may well be proud of her ! "

" By the order I bear of knighthood," answered that other lord, " I shall tell thee truth. If the whole world, more and less, of christendom and heathendom were searched through, there is none other so fair of face. Her skin is as white as snow, and she blushes redder than the rose ; and no man ever made by God might find or imagine one more lovely ! "

Then said the earl : " By God's grace these words make me sorrowful ! But since thou sayest she is so fair, if thou wilt bring me under safeguard within sight of her, I will forgive thee thy ransom, and will render thee my help and love as long as I live ; and thereto I plight my troth. And as I am a true knight I will give thee also an hundred pounds to buy thee horse and armour."

Sir Tralabas answered : " On that covenant, in this place I plight my troth to thee. I shall hold thy foreward good, and bring thee within sight of her ; and thereof will I keep my counsel, and never more, without fail, will be against thee. I shall be true, by God's mercy, even to the losing of my life ! Trust to me boldly ! "

The earl answered him with all courtesy : " Doubtless, I trust to thee as to my friend. Let us busk ourselves anon for our journey to see that woman. I swear, by God and St. Andrew, that if I find thee true, for thee riches shall abound ! "

The two knights stayed not for wind or weather, but rode forth on their way, and never stopped or rested till they came to the city wherein was the empress.

The earl, although he was great of kin, for dread that he might be known, clad himself in hermit's weeds. For three days he dwelled there content, and rested him ; then on the fourth day, he was near betrayed by the knight, who went forthwith to the empress's chamber, and falling on his knee said : " May He that harrowed hell keep you from all danger, if it be His will ! Madam, by Jesus, I have here our worst enemy, the Earl of Toulouse."

"In what manner is he come?" said the lady. "Tell me anon, I prithee."

"Madam," he answered, "I was in his prison, but he has forgiven me my ransom, for love of thee, by Almighty God! Madam, he longs sorely to see thee once. And I am to have as a reward an hundred pounds to buy armour and a noble steed, for I plighted my troth that he should gaze on thee his fill; but, lady, as he is our foe, and hath done us much harm, I rede that we slay him!"

"But," said the lady, "as I live, thy soul is lost if thou do so! Thou must fulfil thy word. Since he forgave thee thy ransom and loosed thee out of prison, put away thy wicked will. To-morrow, when thou hearest the mass-bell ring, bring him to my chapel, with no thought of treachery, and he shall gaze on me as he will, to fulfil thy covenant. Certes, if thou betray him thy soul is in sore peril, since thou hast given him thine oath; and certes, it were a great treason and shame to thee to lie in wait for him!"

Then the knight went to the earl, holding himself but ill sped in his evil intent, and he said: "Sir, as I live, to-morrow thou shalt see my lady, and so be not dismayed. When we hear the mass-bell, I shall bring thee to her chapel. Stand thou by the oriel,[1] and thou shalt gaze upon her fairness as thou wilt."

"I hold thee for true," answered the earl, "and so far

[1] Not window, but porch or gallery.

forth as I may, thou shalt never repent it." Glad at heart he cried : " Fill up the wine ! This goes to my liking ! "

He rested there that night, and on the morrow he clad him in hermit's array, and when the mass-bell rang they two went to the chapel, and had waited there scarcely so long as half a mile might be run when the lady came. She was clad wonder richly in cloth of gold and fine furs ; and when the earl beheld her, he thought her as bright as the blossom on the tree. Of all the sights he had ever seen, none had raised his heart so high. She stood still in that place, and showed him her face openly ; and he swore, by God's mercy, that he had seen none so fair. Her eyes were grey as any glass, her mouth and nose were right shapely, and from forehead to toe no woman might be more graceful. Twice she turned her about between the goodly earls that were with her, that this lord might see her well. And when she spoke most sweetly, she seemed like an angel from heaven. Fair was she, and long and slim and slender of waist, with most lovely arms and shoulders, her hands as white as ivory, with bright fingers and shining nails.

When he had beheld her, she went into the chapel to hear mass, and he followed, unable to take his eyes from her lovely face.

" Lord God All-powerful," he thought, " if I were so worthy a knight as to be her lover, and she had no husband, all the gold that ever God made would not be so dear to me ! "

When the mass was ended, that lovely, gracious lady turned to go back to her chamber.

The earl sighed heavily as she was passing from his sight, and said : " So God save me, I would fain beg alms of her, if it were her will !   If I had something of hers to look upon every day, it might lead to my mending ! "   And so he kneeled down, and prayed to Almighty God that died on the Tree.

Thereupon the empress called a knight, and said : " Bring me anon forty bright florins."   These she gave to the hermit, and slipped a ring from her finger in among the gold.

Thereupon he thanked her many times, and she returned to her chamber where she was liefest to be ; and he went home to his inn.   When he found the ring, he was full of joy and blithe of heart, and kissed it many times, saying : " My dear darling, this is from thy finger—well for me to have so much grace !   If ever I should so come into thy favour that there should be love between us, this shall be our tokening ! "

At daybreak he took leave, and went his way homeward to his own country ; but first he thanked Sir Tralabas : " Well shalt thou be requited for this deed thou hast done for me ! "

They kissed as good friends, and Sir Tralabas—curse him !—went home ; but he thought ever to work some treachery if he could, so evil was he of heart.   Anon he

called two bold knights, his kinsmen both. " Sirs," he
said, " without fail, if ye do after my counsel, ye shall have
great renown.   Know ye the Earl of Toulouse ?   He hath
wrought us much injury ; let us stop his boasting.   If ye
will do as I rede he shall die this day, as God shall save me
from sin ! "

Now one of these knights was called Kantres,[1] the other
Kaym ; [1] and certes, no falser men might be found than
they were.   Sir Tralabas made the third—there was no
need to bid him follow the earl.   They met him at a
bridge, and there set upon him with hard strokes as foemen.   But the earl was a mighty man, and he fought
furiously against them, and soon had killed two, while the
third fled, puffing and panting.   But the earl quickly
overtook him, and clove his head in three.

Meanwhile the whole country-side had gathered and
chased him hotly—an hundred men.   The good earl was
aghast and fain to flee, and passed from them into a
wilderness to rest him a while, being sore wearied.   All
that night he lay in the wood, having no other lodgment,
and when it dawned he rose up and thanked God that sits
on His throne, that he had escaped his foes.   So he
travelled on all that day, many a mile, and often in peril
on the road, until he came to his own fair castle, where he
loved best to dwell.

His people were glad of his coming, and he bade them :

[1] See note.

" Be merry, my men, and spare nothing ! For," said he, " I trow the emperor will now let us be in peace, and war on us no more." And so the earl dwelled at home with mirth and game and laughter, as he loved best. Let us leave him so, and tell how Dame Beaulybon was brought into sorrow.

The emperor loved his wife as well as he did himself, and chose two knights to guard her night and day, whether he were far or near ; and first one, then the other, of these two knights loved her for her fairness and beauty. Neither knew of the other man's secret, although it so wrought upon them both that they nearly died.

It befell on a day that one said to the other : " Sir, as I live, methinks thou fadest quite away as one that is dead and buried. Thy face is as pale as wax ! "

Then said the other : " I avow, right so thou farest, me-thinks, whysoever it may be. Tell me the cause thereof, and certes, I will tell thee mine, I plight my troth ! "

" I grant thee," said the other, " without fail. Look it be true counsel." And thereto he plighted his troth, saying : " I am in great unpeace for love of our lady, the empress ! It will drive me to death ! "

And the other said : " Verily, beyond a doubt, so fare I for love of that bright dame ! And since both our hearts are set on her, how may our trouble best be amended ? Canst thou counsel wisely ? "

" By St. John," sware the first, " methinks I know no

"Tell me thy secret — why thou mournest so still?"

better rede than this, that one of us go secretly to her and entreat her love. I myself will try first, and in case I find favour thou shalt not miss thy share, for thou shalt take us together, and lest thou betray us she will fear and grant thee thy will."

Thus they were of one assent ; and the false thief went forth to learn the lady's mind. He found her in her chamber, and set him on his knee to carry out his purpose.

" Stand up, sir knight," quoth the lady. " Who hath vexed thee at any time ? It shall go ill with whomso-ever hath wronged thee. Tell me thy secret—why thou mournest so still ? "

" Lady," says he, " by great God invisible, that I durst not for all the gold that ever was wrought ! But if ye will swear on the Book not to discover me, then it might be possible."

The lady answered : " How is this, that thou darest not trust me ? It is horrible ! But here I plight thee my troth, and I shall keep it night and day, as true as book or bell ! "

" Lady, in you is my trust. I would ye knew what pain I suffer for your sake ! I droop and pine, night and day ! My wit and my will are all gone except ye believe my words. Many a day have I loved you, but never durst tell you—my grief has been the more ! Except ye grant to me your favour, certes, I am but dead, and I set no store by my life ! "

Then answered that lovely lady: " Sir, well thou knowest I am a wife, and my lord is the emperor, who chose thee for a true knight to keep me always in thy ward. If I consented to your will I were worthy to be burnt and brought into great dole ! By sweet Mary, thou art a traitor, and shouldst be hanged and drawn ! "

" Ah, madam," said the knight, " for love of Almighty God, give no heed to what I have said ; ye may trust me still. God save me, I spoke but to frighten you. Remember, madam, your troth is plight to keep my counsel. I cry you mercy, for God's sake ; and if ever I talk more hereof, let me be dragged by a horse ! "

" I forgive thee," answered the lady, " and as long as I live I will keep thy secret ; but look thou be henceforth a true man, in every way, to my lord."

" Yes, lady, else did I ill, for I have served him long time, and well hath he requited me."

He said no more, but presently returned to his companion, who asked : " Sir, how hast thou sped ? "

" Not at all," he answered. " Dear brother, I have never been so afeared since the day I was born ! Certes, it is trouble thrown away to bring her such a tale, at board or in chamber."

" That," said the other, " is because of thy thin wit. I wager my head I will win her ! "

Thus it passed over until the third day after this, when the second knight bethought him : " Certes, speed as I may, I will try the mind of my sweet lady." And when he saw her in her best mood, he went to her with bitter sighing, as if he recked naught of life, and said : " Lady, except ye help me with your counsel, I shall be brought to my ending ! "

She answered kindly : " My counsel is ready—tell me how it is. If any word of mine can mend the matter, it shall, as I have hope of bliss ! "

" Lady," quoth he, " ye must hold up your hand, faithfully to keep my secret."

" Yes," says that noble lady, " thereto I plight my troth, and else I did amiss."

" Madam," he answered, " now I can trust you ; I know you would never betray me. For you, dear lady, am I brought into great sorrow—I swear without oath ! Ye can see how pale I am. I am near dying of my hurt. For the sake of God on high that was stung by a spear, grant me thy love ! "

" Sir," she said, " is that thy will ? If it were mine, I should be well to blame ! What kind of woman holdest thou me to be ? What hast thou heard or seen in me sith I have been in thy keeping, that touches on villainy, and makes thee as bold of heart as though I were a light woman or a shrew ? Had I not promised to keep counsel, thou shouldst certainly have been hanged on the gallows-tree ! "

At this the knight was so adread as never before since

he was born on Middle-Earth.[1] "Mercy, good madam," he cried, "well I know I am to blame, and my heart is woe! Lady, let me not be shent![2] I cry you mercy for my guilt—spare my life!"

"I grant thee to keep thy secret," said the lady, "but do no more so."

Then the knight went forth, and said: "Fellow, I may not speed. What is thy best counsel? If she tell my lord of this, as I hope for bliss we are but dead! Woman's tongue is ill to trust! Certes, my friend, an my lord knew of this, our bread were all eaten! But ere she shall bring us to that woe, she shall die herself!"

"How might that be?" asked the other. "I should be well pleased were it done."

"Yes, sir," he answered, "have no fear; I shall bring her to it. Ere three days be passed she shall be in sorrow enough, and so will I repay her!" And now are they both of one mind to bring that gentle lady into woe—the devil speed them!

Presently it drew towards night, and the empress and her men went to supper, where these knights made great jokes to amuse the lovely, graceful lady. When supper time was done, they two, in their garments of rich pall, entered the chamber, and danced and revelled as though they had no fear, until it was time for the lady to go to bed—foul befall them!

[1] See note on *Floris and Blancheflour*, p. 180.   [2] Undone.

Now there was a certain young knight, twenty years of age, an earl's son and carver to the lady, who was a fair child and bold; and to him said that one thief: " Sir, if thou wilt do as we tell thee, we shall arrange a play for my lady, so to make her laugh that even if she were thy foe, she should become thy friend."

The child answered anon: " By the order I bear of knight, gladly! To please my lady, I would put myself to any misease, even running for her in wind and rain!"

" Then, sir, strip save thy breeks, and creep behind yonder curtain, and do as I tell thee, and so shalt thou see a pretty play."

" I grant you," said the young knight, " by God and St. Germain!"

" Whatso befall," they said to him, " come not out till we call thee;" and he: " Sirs, I assent."

When they had revelled for some while, no man knowing of their device save they two, they cleared the chamber, and left the child sitting there alone with the gentle lady, who lay down in her bed to sleep with no thought of treason.

The child wondered greatly why the knights were so long, and had many thoughts: " Lord a' mercy! How is this? I trow, they that brought me hither have forgotten me. If I call them, by Him that created all things, my lady here in her bed will be afeared!" And so he sat as still as any stone, and durst not stir or cry out for fear of affrighting the lady.

These false men—eternal woe be theirs !—went to their chamber, and arming themselves fully, called the lords from their beds, and bade them, great and small: "Hasten ye anon to take a traitor that hath been this whole night with my lady in her bower ! "

As soon as the lords were armed, they went with these traitors to the empress's chamber, with swords and torches burning bright before them. And there behind the curtain they found the young child, whom straightway one false knight thrust through the body with a battle-sword, so that he spoke never word more.

The lady awoke afeared when she saw the great light by her bedside. " Benedicite ! " she said, and cried wonder loud : " Sirs, what men are ye ? "

And her foes answered at once : " We are here, thou false woman ! We have discovered thy deeds ! Thou hast deceived our lord, and thy evil fame shall be known far and wide throughout the world ! "

" By St. John," cried the lady, " I was never false, nor ever thought to be ! "

" Thou liest," they said, " and thy good name is lost ! " Thereupon they laid the body before her : " Lo, here is thy lover. Thus have we dealt with him for thy sake, and thy falseness shall be well requited ; thou shalt not escape us ! " With that they bound her wonder fast, and cast her into deep prison, so that it was a piteous sight to behold.   There let us leave her, and see how it was with her lord, who was far away.

One night in his sleep, he dreamed that there came two wild bears, which tore his wife in twain ; and being a man of sense, he knew from that dream that his lady was in trouble.   As soon as the clear day broke, he bade his men busk [1] and make them yare.[2]   First, he sent on pack-horses and chariots laden with goods, a train twelve miles long and more.   Although he hoped well that she was not in any danger, yet he was so heavy of heart that he stayed not by night or day, until with his earls and barons he was on the homeward road ; and then he never rested until he came to the city where she was.

The lords remained outside the town, and many of them wept without ceasing for pity of that lady ; they thought that if he but knew she had such a hurt, his joy would be thin enough.

The emperor's horses were led into their stalls, and he himself was brought with high state into the hall.   Anon he went into the chamber to see his fair lady that was so sweet and good, and called out to those that guarded her : " Where is my wife ?   Is she asleep ?   How fareth that bright dame ? "

Straightway the two traitors answered : " If ye knew what she hath done, she would be put to death ! "

" The devil ! " he cried.   " How so ?   She worthy of death ?   Tell me in what way ! "

[1] Prepare.   [2] Ready.

I.

" Sire," they said, " the young knight, Sir Antore,[1] that was her carver, lay with her ; but we found them together, and slew him, and put her into prison. And by God that bought us dear, the law saith she should be burned ! "

" Alas ! " cried the emperor, " hath she done me such dishonour and I loved her so well ? I deemed she had not been faithless for all this world's goods ! My joy grows cold ! "

He seized a knife with might and main, and would have killed himself had not a knight held him. Out of his wit with grief, he threw up his arms and fell swooning on his bed ; and there indeed might men see great dole.

On the morrow, by common accord, they called a parliament on her ; but they could find no law whereby she might be saved from death.

Then an old knight spoke out : " I wonder, by God's might, that Sir Antore was thus set upon in the chamber, defenceless. By my head, they let him give no answer, but slew him forthwith. I dare well say that no other man save those two ever suspected him of villainy. It may be for some grudge. Therefore, for my sake, do as I counsel, I pray you. None can prove her guilt except these knights ; and so, although we may not save her altogether from her woe, we may find some good man to fight against the two in her quarrel."

To that saying all assented, as it seemed both reason and

[1] See note.

law ; and the emperor in his crown, cried : " Fair befall thee for thy counsel ! "

Then he called knights of prowess and bade them be boun[1] to proclaim through all the land, by sea and by shore, if perchance they might find a man daring enough to undertake the fight for that lady. And he bade them say that if any man should offer himself, he should be well rewarded. So messengers cried throughout the land in many a great city, that if any man durst prove his strength to fight in a true quarrel, he should be advanced in his estate.

Now the Earl of Toulouse heard tell of the trouble that had befallen this lady, and him thought it sore pity. If he knew that she had right, he was willing to risk his life in battle for her. He mourned for her day and night, and said to himself that he would venture : " If I may learn that she be true, they that accused her shall repent them unless they stint of their strife ! " He vowed : " By St. John, I will go into Almayne where my foemen are thick ; and I pray to Almighty God that I have a true quarrel to fight in to bring that lady out of her woe ! "

One day as he rode a-hunting, he met a merchant by the way, and asked him whence he was come.

" Lord," he said, " from Almayne."

Thereupon the earl questioned him of that case : " Wherefore is your empress put to such distress ? Tell me, for God's sake ! As thou livest, is she guilty ? "

[1] Ready.

" Nay, by Him that died on the Tree and formed man in His image ! "

" Then," said the earl, " when is the day set that she be burned ? "

" Even to-day three weeks," answered the merchant. " Woe is me ! "

" I have some horses to sell," quoth the earl, " and certes, if I could dispose of them there, I would go with thee to see that sight."

" It would be to your advantage," said the merchant courteously, " to go into that land, for there ye may sell them to your liking."

" Listen to me, sir," said the earl anon.   " Shall we go together this journey ?   I will give thee a reward of twenty pounds, I vow."

" By St. John, I grant you ! "

Upon this, the earl told him where to wait, and trusted him utterly, and then went home and busked him, so that none of his men knew of it.   " Now, sir," he said, " come with me."

With them they took seven fine horses, as fair as any that man might see under heaven ; and they rode with them together into Almayne, so that the earl seemed to be a horse-dealer of goodly estate.

The merchant was a true guide, and he and the earl rode on until they came within a mile of the castle wherein dwelled the emperor.

There stood a rich abbey where they got leave to sojourn and fatten their horses—a fine excuse ! And the abbot himself was the lady's uncle ; wherefore he was in great tribulation and mourned heavily.

It befell on a day that the earl went to church for to hear Mass ; and when the abbot remarked how he was a fair man and tall, he said : " Sir, draw nigh, and when Mass is done, I pray you, eat with me at noon, if it be your will." And to this the earl assented gladly.

So they washed and went to meat ; and after dinner they walked together in an orchard, and the abbot said, sighing sorely : " In truth, sir, my heart is deeply troubled for a bright lady who is wrongfully accused, and shall be burned in a fire, this day seven-night, but she have help ! "

" As I hope for heaven, methinks it is great pity of her, if she be true," answered the earl.

" By St. Paul," quoth the abbot, " I dare wager my soul she was never guilty, either in thought or in deed. She did never aught, save that once she graciously gave a ring to the Earl of Toulouse ; but it was to ease his heart, and not for any sin, as she herself told me in shrift."

" Since that is true," says the earl, " may Christ avenge her on her foes ! If ye would pledge yourself to keep my counsel, it might be for your good."

The abbot swore by many books and his profession that he would keep the secret, and else he were mad.

" I am he to whom she gave the ring for a token.   Conceal it, for the Rood! And I am come, dear sir, to take the battle for her, and to stand by the right; but first I would myself shrive her, and if I find her clean in her life, my heart will be glad! Let me be dressed in a monk's robe, and taken to the place where they will lead her forth to die; and when I have shriven her, there without fail will I fight the battle for her!"

Thereupon was the abbot near mad for joy. He kissed the earl, and they made merry together; and they slew care in mirth that was none so amiss, all the seven-night that the earl dwelled in that place.

On the day that the lady should be burned, the earl, in monk's robe, went with the abbot, and straightway kneeled to the emperor and begged that he might shrive her, and was granted. But although he examined her utterly, he found her without guilt.

"By Him that died on the Tree," she said, "I have done no sin wherefore I should be put to death! Once only—assoil me if thou wilt—I gave a ring to the Earl of Toulouse. But so my destiny is concluded; I must perish in the fire and do the will of God."

The earl assoiled her with his hand; and then stood up briskly, and said: "Peace, lords! Ye that have accused this gentle lady deserve to be burned!"

One of the two knights started up: "Thou churlish monk, though thine abbot be of her kin, thou shalt not for all thy cunning, free her from her pain! Right so wouldst thou have said, though all thy monastery had lain by her, so false art thou and wicked ! "

Boldly the earl answered : " Sir, I trow ye be that one who hath accused this lady. Though we be men of religion, ye shall do us but right for all the fare ye make. I will prove that ye speak falsely of her—lo, here is my glove ! I undertake this battle, and I shall make you known for false men, and ye shall burn in this fire, as may God lend me grace ! "

And all that were present thanked God of His mercy.

The two knights were full of rage, and swore great oaths that he should die ; but they might not avail, for he went aside and armed himself proudly to attack them. Full manly they met together, and smote through helmet and head-piece, and marred much under mail. And as they rode, one broke his spear against the earl, and the other missed him. One the earl smote through the body and bore to the ground. The other beheld and fled; but the earl overtook him by a tree, and wrought him much hurt ; whereupon the traitor, unable to escape, yielded him up as a miscreant in the field. He was brought before the emperor, and there made to confess. He said : " We devised to slay that noble dame because she would not do our will."

The earl answered him : " Therefore, traitors, ye shall burn both at once in this fire ! " And anon they were so destroyed, skin, flesh, and bones.

As soon as this was done, the earl stole away to the abbey, while with glee and mirth they fetched the lady in procession back into the town.

The emperor said in his joy, " Bring me that monk. Why went he so away ? I will give him a bishopric, and my help and love as long as I live, by God that owns this day ! "

The abbot kneeled on his knee, excusing him : " Lord, he is gone away to his own land. He dwells with the Pope of Rome, who will be glad of his return, I assure you."

" Sir abbot," said the emperor, " it dishonours me to hear such words ! Send after him in all haste, else shall ye never more have goods of mine. Thereto my hand ! "

" Lord," said the abbot, " since it be so, I will go after him myself. But ye must pledge me that if he hath been your foe, ye will do him no harm. As I hope to thrive, I will fetch him, so please you, if you promise to be his friend."

" Yes," says the emperor, full fain, " though he had slain all my kindred, he is welcome to me ! "

Then spake the abbot boldly : " Lord, now I trust in you, that ye will do as ye say. It is Sir Barnard of Toulouse, that noble and chivalrous knight, who hath done this day's work."

" Certes," said the emperor, " the more dishonour to me ! Anon, sir, I pray you, follow after him ; and we shall kiss and be friends for God's sake that owns this day!"

The abbot answered, " I grant it ! "   Then he went to
the earl, saying : " Sir, come with me.   By St. John, my
lord and yourself shall be made of accord to be good
friends."   And of that the earl was full fain.

" My noble friend," said the emperor, coming to meet
him, " my anger against thee is gone ; and while I live I
will cherish thee, by Him that died on the Tree ! "

They kissed together lovingly, as the romance tells us,
and all men rejoiced.   The emperor made the earl his
steward, and seised again in his hand the possessions whereof
he had bereft him.

After this the emperor lived but three years longer ;
and the earl by the election of the nobles was made
emperor in his stead, being a man stiff in battle against
his foes.

He wedded the lady, and they led their life together in
joy and mirth for three-and-twenty years ; and they had
fifteen children, seemly to look at, who became doughty
knights all.

> *In Rome this geste chronicled is,*
> *A lay of Britain called it is,*
> > *And ever more shall be.*
> *Jesus Christ to heaven us bring,*
> *There to have our dwelling,*
> > *Amen, amen for charity !*

SIR DEGREVANT

Lord God in Trinity,
Grant them Heaven for to see
That love a story or a glee,
  And jesters [1] for to feed!
When folk are met together in hall,
They should hearken, one and all,
To tales of old, that did befall,
  Of brave men good at need.

Now I shall tell you of a knight
That hardy was and thereto wight;
Sir Degrevant was his name aright,
  That doughty was of deed.
Was never a king in the tourney's play,
In France or England any day,
Might send the shaft from his hand away,
  When stiff he sat on steed.

Now this knight was known to King Arthur and Queen
Guinevere as a bold man; and his prowess was famous far
and wide in heathendom, and in Spain, France, and
Brittany, together with the renown of Perceval and
Gawain. He was nephew to the king and queen,[2] and
wherever he heard tell of adventures, thither he went,

---

[1] Or *gesters*, professional tellers of tales.   [2] See note.

until presently he was made a knight of the Round Table, as is shown in the *Mappa Mundi.*[1]

He was also greatly given to music, harp and psaltery, and gay gittern,[2] and he had always the prize for playing on the rote [3] and the lute, and for his sweet singing. Yet was he a lover of sport, and kept greyhounds for hunting the hare and hart and buck and bear, day and night. Many fair falcons and hawks of noble eyries flocked in his parks, sixty together. He would be up ere the dawn to hunt and ride, and every day brought him fresh sport ; but always he went first to hear Mass, with good intent. Afterwards, he rode in the forest with horn and hound to bring down the deer, for that was his chief joy. Certes, he had never wished for wife or wench ; but had lived always as true as the anchor in a stone.[4]

He held in his possession a thousand pounds' worth of land, and of goodly rents a great deal more. In his demesnes were an hundred ploughlands, and fair parks enclosed in hedges, great herds in the plains and a mighty store of tame beasts, high-walled castles with noble halls and chambers, and fair steeds in his stables, both lyard [5] and sorrel. And he never heard any cry but that he busked him, and rode anon into the land whence it came.

He loved well alms-deeds, clothed and fed poor men, and was free of his meat ; and also he called for *gestes,*[6] and

---

[1] See note.   [2] A sort of guitar.   [3] A small harp.
[4] See note.   [5] Dappled grey or white.   [6] Stories.

to the minstrels in his hall gave rich robes, gold and other fee.

Wherever he went in his journeyings from home, they blessed his name and held it in honour ; and in every land, so many had he hurt in jousts and tournaments that he won always the prize.

Near him there dwelled an earl, a proud lord that owned seven wide forests and many bowers. He was jealous of the knight for his great prowess, and being himself fierce and stalwart, he rode with a gay rout of henchmen and broke into his best parks and therein made sorry play, and killed the fattest bucks in the field, sixty at a time. Likewise, he fished in Degrevant's rivers and slew his foresters.

Now all this was unknown to the knight, as I need not tell you, for he was at that time in the Holy Land doing valiant deeds of arms against the heathen. But his steward sent him a letter by a messenger who rode as swiftly as he might ride.

Without tarrying, the knight busked him and rode away from Granada [1] as fast as he could ; and within a twelve-night he and his men had overpassed the sea and come into his own country.

He went straightway to his manor, and found that fair place all despoiled ; his husbandmen that paid rent were harried outright, and the best tenantry in his towns were

---

[1] See note.

ruined, and his goodly parks were turned into common,
and in an evil state.

He enclosed his parks again, and lent the husbandmen
oxen and wains from his own store, and also seed for sow-
ing, and strong draught-horses ; and thought to proceed
by law and by no other means. Therefore he wrote a
letter to the mighty earl, and prayed him do right or tell
him wherefore ; and this he sent by a squire that was
worth an hundred pounds rent.

Now this squire rode fast towards the palace of pride
wherein dwelled the earl, Sir Sere of Cypirs,[1] but chanced
to meet him with many a knight, busked for hunting in the
forest. So stern and stout was that lord, and had so
strong a company that the squire feared to abide the first
brunt of the meeting.   But as soon as they drew near, and
their horses stood front to front, he greeted the earl and
his barons with fair words.

Holding the letter by one corner, the squire gave it to
the earl, who glanced at it and then spoke his mind :
" Wert thou not a messenger, thou shouldst abuy this,
right here in the woodland !   Only to vex thy proud lord,
I will hunt in his forests and his greens,[2] and will break
open his parks when I like ! "

Then said the squire : " Sir, that is not well done.
Truly now ye have left him but the one course, as every
just man would say, be he knight or squire : here is my

---

[1] See note.   [2] Grass lands.

glove, whatsoever befall ! Sir, so please you, remember ye have done ill. I counsel you to amend it by reason, for woes spread ever wide ! "

But the earl answered : " I will amend nothing ! For all his pride, I count him not worth a cress ! " He waxed wroth, and swore mightily that the squire should be a sorry messenger unless he went his way ; and this he might not deny, so he took his leave and rode off, as fast as he might, over the broad bent.[1]

He arrived home at nones,[2] and told how he had fared ; and the knight asked him what answer had been sent.

" Sir, an he may do as he intends, he will never stint [3] his game ; and if once he get you into his power, I hold you for lost ! "

Then Sir Degrevant sighed and looked up to heaven : " Jesus, save my right, and Mary speed me ! I vow to God some of us shall rue it ! And he shall not come out well, if I rede aright ! "

Anon they geared them with weapons as fast as might be, and knight and squire alike donned strong armour. In a short while, were ten score ready, and with them three hundred archers good at need. Presently they rode into the forest, and there galloped a while ere they pitched their pavilions and rested for the night.

On the other side, the earl purveyed him a host, and

---

[1] Grassy plain ; sometimes grass.

[2] Three P.M.   [3] Stop.

came along with many a fierce knight bragging and boasting. Within Degrevant's boundaries he uncoupled his
hounds, and harried all at once his parks and his greens.
Thus they crashed through the forest, set harts at bay, and
finally dismounted in a glade under a hill. Sixteen harts
they had brought down and slain before their chieftain.

Then said the dukes on that land : " Where is now Sir
Degrevant ? Why comes that giant not to rescue his
deer ? No peace-charter shall save his proud fat harts.
We shall have got a few of them ere we stop ! I would he
were here ! Truly ere he went away, he should repent him
of his game and of the proud letter that he sent by his
squire ! "

Now Sir Degrevant was so near that he overheard, and
cried out : " Forward, banners, and trumpets blow ! "
And his archers stood all ready to shoot.

The earl was pleased, and quickly arrayed him for battle,
being nothing afraid of that fierce knight. And now they
meet in the field, with spear and buckler ; and mightily
they use their weapons in savage combat. As soon as they
came together, they lunged with their lances so that no
man in the field might be spared. With their glittering
swords they rent rich hauberks on the bent, and shining
glaives gleamed against golden shields. They thrust steeds
in that stour,[1] and goodly knights were hurt through
their armour on those heathery [2] hills. So fiercely they

---

[1] Battle.   [2] See note.

fought that none wist, save He that rules all, who should have the victory.

The bold knight Degrevant brought many a lord low to the ground, pierced through jerkin and coat-of-mail, and many he lamed. Many a glittering shield was shattered and many a doughty man died under his rich armour all red with blood. Thus they struggled in that frith,[1] and brought many a stout man to his death, these bold fellows with their kinsfolk,[2] in wreaking vengeance. Many a mother's bairn was laid low, groaning under his gambison [3] on the brown bent, and died under his steed. And ever Degrevant burnished bacinets [4] bright, and his friends fought fiercely and beat down his foes.

All the earl's knights that were held for chivalrous and strong in battle, perished at that time. He himself kept aloof, and watched how they fared with shield and lance, and sighed heavily to see the best men that ever he led left as pledges on the field. He himself took to flight with fifty spearmen, being sore wounded.

Sir Degrevant and his men chased them like deer through the fens, and down in the hollows he dang them to death. With sharp steel axes he hacked their bacinets bright; and for many a knight he garred a knell to be rung in the morning. And he was vexed when the battle parted a-two.

---

[1] Enclosed wood or field.   [2] See note.
[3] Jerkin.   [4] Helmets; *i.e.*, with his sword.

As for the earl, right sorrowfully he sprang to horse and fled away, leaving behind him in the hollow, forty score slain in a heap, with gaping wounds in their backs, lying dead in the ling. But yet Sir Degrevant got him a horse good at need, and pierced many a side with his spear's dint, and chased the earl hotly for more than eleven miles. Many a man did he repay that before had done him hurt.

At last he came jogging home, and was fain to find none of his folk dead or a jot the worse. In that very place, he kneeled down and thanked God for His mercy; and so they all returned to his fair manor.

> *Here endeth the first fit.*[1]
> *How say ye ?   Will ye more of it ?*

II

Presently knight and squire went to supper, and blithe of heart, danced and revelled all that night.

But the earl came home, disgraced and wounded; and his lady, seeing him lame, swooned away and cried often : " Alas, have ye not parks and chases of your own ? What should ye be doing in that place to pay such a price ? "

" Dame," he answered, " I was there, and I rue it! And I take my leave for ever of righting such wrongs ! "

On the morrow, Sir Degrevant geared him whenso he would on a Barbary horse,[2] and armed at all points, rode

---

¹ Canto.   ² See note.

I.

with his men to the barbican of the earl's castle. There he halted and dismounted in lordly wise, and asked, was there any within would render to him and twelve knights three courses of war in that place? He prayed the porter to take his message and bring an answer, and had a promise thereof.

Anon the porter went into the hall and said to the earl: "Here is come to your gate the good knight Sir Degrevant armed upon a steed, and with him are many bold men and stout, in weeds of war and high glittering helmets. He demands jousts of battle, and prays you for an answer; and I must needs be his messenger."

The earl said hastily: "Here is none ready!" It would seem that this doughty man feared Sir Degrevant.

Then came the countess into the hall, and with her her daughter, who was gentle and slim and lovesome to look upon. She gazed out upon the adventurous man, and said: "Sir knight, ye are a marvel, I plight my word! But if God hath lent you grace to overcome your foes, do not on that account come hither to seek us out, or night or day."

He answered that noble lady: "Madam, blame not me; ill-fortune is his that fights in the wrong! My parks were all destroyed and my rivers dragged, and I am greatly enangered! While I was fighting in Spain, he made my lands bare, both wood and warren; and he loosed my game. I tell you without fear, he that dealt with me so shall be quit his meed,[1] even if I die in the plain ! He that slew my foresters shall make good, as soon as I may bring it about ! "

Then she spoke wisely from the hall : " Ye have already slain good men ; I rede that ye accord ere any more die."

But he answered in haste : " As I walk on the earth, he that did me such villainy shall abide his bargain ! Madam, so please you, take it not ill ; I am bound to fight my foe ! I tell you in truth, it shall not end so lightly ! Many a brave man shall die yet ere it be concluded ! "

The knight waited in the field with axe and buckler ; and the earl's daughter saw that he was a bold man and burly. He was armed in gold and azure sheen, set with true-loves,[2] gay to see. And she was comely clad, that fair maiden, as she walked between two bannerets,[3] and was sweet to fold in arms. She turned the knight's thoughts to love, and he promised his own heart that he would be her servant, prosper as he might.

However that was to be, he took his leave then : " Madam, hold not amiss what I tell you. Greet the earl, your father, and say that we shall never be at one till he have restored my things that he hath taken away. Heretofore he might easily have made his peace with me ; but now I defy him to the teeth, for all his great array ! I swear that, but for your sake, I should wake him finely

---

[1] Given what he deserves.   [2] True-love knots.
[3] Knights banneret. See note.

ere to-morrow dawned! But for my gentlehood, I scorn to do such robberies as to make affray at the castles of fair ladies; and sith I may no more, I will go to his enclosures and spare no wild beast all this day!"

Anon they rode away into the forest with horn and hounds, to bring down the deer where they lay in the glades. And so he began his sport; his hunting-dogs ran royally, and he had felled sixty bucks ere he ceased. And ere he rested, he had done his worst to the earl, and had hunted through his forests with bold men. He drew his deep ditches, killed his white swans, and got as many great luces [1] as he would.

But now him likes no mirth or revel, since for maid Melidore's [2] sake he hath fallen into heavy care.

One day at the hunting, he told his squire how it was, and that he loved a damsel sweet to embrace: "My love is fallen loyally on a lady bright as beryl and crystal-clear. She is wise and prudent; and her lily-face is run with red as the rose on its branch! She is far the fairest of women, in her rich raiment! Once only I came near enough to see her on a wall; but I had liefer she were mine than all the Rhine-gold [2] fashioned into florins— so dear hath she grown to me!"

His squire answered: "Let me but know who she is, and on pain of death I assure you, if in any wise I can, I will win that maid to be your wife. And here I swear

[1] Pikes.   [2] See note.

never to reveal your secret. And while my body may endure, I will fight faithfully with knife or sword, against squire or knight that would be your rival!"

"Her name is Melidore, and she is white as the foam of the sea! My bold fellows would blame me—what good to lie? And yet must I make my vows against all men's counsel, for my life or death is in her hands! Although she is the earl's only heir, I would ask nothing of his, neither castle nor town[1]—naught save her own sweet self, and we to be friends evermore! How great is my sorrow!"

The squire counselled him: "Remember that ye are foes, and let some prudent man go between you in this need. For I dare safely swear that if he took you captive, all England here would speak of your death. It is but folly to love your foe, if ye get only damage and ill-will for your meed. Or again, ladies would say: 'Might no other woman please you but that proud maiden, Melidore?'"

But Sir Degrevant answered: "Thou shalt never say that I am recreant to friend or foe; for thou wouldst hold me mad or else afraid of the earl. Dost thou think I will leave my love so easily? Arm thee well at eventide in iron and steel, for we shall to the castle, our two selves alone. This very night, be it for weal or woe, I will speak with that bright lady!"

[1] See note.

So they mounted two strong coursers, and presently alighted under a lime-tree near a glade. At daybreak, the earl, with his proud knights, busked him on his way out by a postern and into the forest for sport.

Sir Degrevant did not move until the earl had passed the hill, then he said quietly to his squire : " I rede we hasten through that postern and hide until the lady comes."

He took no further heed, but went in. The porter had been sore afraid had he been at the gate ; but he was gone away to sleep. Armed as they were, they ran into an orchard, and there rested behind a rose-bush until the day waxed clear, undern [1] and later. Then the chapel-bell began to ring, and the gay damsel made her ready for the service.

She came clad in violet,[2] fretted over with white pearls and set with sapphires ; and the stuff was of fine pall,[3] furred with ermine, and left open for pride. It were hard to count her buttons, all enamelled with azure, topaz, and other gems ; and at her side gleamed a ribbon of red gold. Her hair was gathered under a splendid gold crown set with bosses, and she had a frontal [4] of Orient pearls that had been sent to her from Cyprus. Her kerchiefs were

---

[1] Nine A.M., also nine to twelve.
[2] See note.
[3] Fine cloth, originally always, as here, purple.
[4] Ornament for the forehead.

curious about her sweet gay face ; and the amorous knight
had great joy when he beheld her.

By the time that Mass was said, the hall was royally
arrayed, and the earl had returned and dismounted in his
court. The trumpeters summoned to meat, and all the
great lords and ladies washed and went to dinner ; but
afterwards, when the boards were taken up, the ladies arose
and returned to the chamber. Only Melidore and her
maid went into the orchard, and came anon where lay Sir
Degrevant. At once he rose and met her in an alley, and
greeted her fair, saying : " Certes, noble lady, may Jesus
save us both ! I would fain be your servant, and plight
troth with you ; and had I time, I would speak with
you secretly, for indeed all my life is locked up in your
grace ! "

Now the lady was greatly afraid, and yet she was pleased
to see that comely knight in splendid array. She answered
anon : " Whether ye be squire or knight, methinks ye do
wrong in coming thus armed as if for war, to fright
maidens a-walking for pleasure in their arbour. By God
and St. James, I know not who ye are, but, i' faith, ye are
greatly to blame ! "

Then the knight kneeled to her : " Madam, so please
you, this have I done, and I may not gainsay it. As may
God save me from sin, by no other device might I get
speech with you, day or night ! If I tell you my name,
I am not at fault if it turn to my undoing ; I am Sir

Degrevant, an so please ye, I would be your lover, as
I am true knight!"

But she cried out: "Traitor, let be! By Him that
died on the Cross, my lord himself shall see you hanged
on high!"

Then Sir Degrevant laughed as he stood under the
bough: "Madam, reproach me as ye will for all the
trouble. I had no guilt for the bloodshed above yonder
hill, and that will I prove to your liking. As ye are the
pink [1] of courtesy and prudence, I put my trust in your
gentlehood. Why will ye do me to death? An I be slain
in this place, ye shall be the cause thereof; and that
would ye rue and like full ill!"

But still she cried: "Traitor, ye shall pay for your
hardihood in doing me this dishonour! Ye shall be
hanged and drawn, for ye have slain our folk; and my
father will be right glad to see that sight!"

Then he said: "Sith it may be no better, go fetch all
his meiny to fight me; but by my word, ere I stop the
gayest of them all shall groan, even if they come forty
strong! I promise you, some that are now dancing lightly
shall be fey, [2] an we fight, for all their great pride!"

The stout man was stirred to wrath, and took his sword
from his squire; and the sweet lady durst abide no longer,
but fled away to her chamber, and swore that he should be

---

[1] See note.
[2] Scotch still: doomed, from O. E. *fǽge*.

undone. But her maiden doffed her hood, and knelt
there : " Madam, on Yule-night, ye did promise me my
gift ; I ask no more but that yonder knight may sleep by
my side."

Belive [1] she was well chidden, but she was not abashed to
ask the same thing again. " Damsel, go do as thou wilt !
I prithee, leave me to my sleep. Go and make merry thy
guest, in the name of all the devils ! But, God save me,
hadst thou asked for my humblest knave, it had been more
to my liking. I swear to thee by God's grace that if ever
he come near me, he will find himself in such a pass as
never before, or night or day ! "

" Madam," she said, " gramercy for your great kind-
ness ! "

Belive a chamber was made ready ; and she fetched in
the knight secretly, unseen of any, as women are cunning
at such work when they like. She prepared for his supper
river-birds and many other dainties, with no lack of spices.
He sat at his ease in a comely coat-of-mail, and the girl
made him good cheer and carved his meat ; but for all
that was cut, he ate never the more, and when he sighed
heavily, the maiden smiled. Soon after he says : " What
doth the earl nowadays ? Doth he hunt or revel, or how
spend his time ? "

And she answers : " Sith all his chivalry was killed, he
hath never passed out on the plain half a mile. His hurts

[1] At once.

have so damaged him that he is sorely afeared ; and the gates have been aye bolted for dread of your guile ! "

" Ere his gates be secure, I shall fright him well ! I shall shake him by the beard the next time we meet—save I let be for her sake that I have chosen for my bride ! She makes me lie awake in sorrow with wet cheeks ! I had liefer she were at peace with me than all his gold ! And if once I had that sweet maid in my arms, then, I swear by my hand, never were emperor or king more to his liking ! "

She answers : " Methinks your labour is to no purpose, for ye have slain our kindred ! So, how may that be ? I swear by God's might, if ever she set eyes upon you again, ye shall be hanged high on a tree ! She is sought by dukes and emperors ; and it were to her shame to marry you ! The Duke of Gerle [1] hath sent word to her that he will hold a tournament, and my lord hath agreed to be there. The duke will come a-jousting in great array ; but by my counsel, ye will not enter that sport. It is my lord's intent that if ye go there, ye and all your men shall perish ! "

" Damsel, ye have doubtless warned me of this deed through great gentlehood—may God repay you ! I swear by St. Luke I shall joust with him till I am rebuffed, how-ever it may be ! Now, damsel, in return for your good cheer and my supper, you shall have my squire—look if that he be pay enough. Here I pledge you[2] four hundred pounds' worth of land to marry her as I bid you."

---

[1] See note.   [2] The squire.

When they were handfasted, torches were set a-burning, and Sir Degrevant gave his squire the order of knighthood.

And after he said : " For God's sake, commend me to my lady and yours, if ye will have my favour to my death's day. Commend me secretly to her, lest she have but a poor opinion of me. I tell you verily, no emperor or knight shall marry her, for I will prevent him ; and I give you my word that since first I saw her I have not slept any night half-an-hour ! Pray that gracious lady to be my friend, and for her honour's sake to send me some help !"

Says the maid : " I take your errand in hand ; and though I be banished for it from this place, I shall stop for no fear ! Now I will show you how to go in and out of the castle for the speeding of your suit. Between the chamber and the hall there is a moat [1] forty feet wide where ye can come in o' nights secretly and unseen ; and ye shall find here your chamber always ready, if I can bring it to pass."

" Damsel, for God's sake, show me that place ! "

Then the maid went first, and led him to a postern, through which he came to a water-gate, where men from boats victualled the castle with corn. " At ebb of tide, ye shall wade not knee-deep."

The knight kissed her, and early on the morrow the two men passed that moat and entered the forest, where they found their horses standing under the hawthorn. And as

[1] See note.

soon as Sir Degrevant came home, he busked all his men
to go to the tournament.   But there let us leave him and
speak of what was said by the bright lady and her maid.

Early that same day, the lady laughed her woman to
scorn : " Thy good name is lost—God give thee care ! "

" Madam, if it be so, it hurts none but me ; and I vouch
me safe with that noble man, if it were so ! "

At this the lady laughed aloud : " Damsel, i' God's
name, how doth he please thee ? "

" I dare boast for Sir Degrevant, that I know none so
courteous, so kindly, so good !   Certainly, yester even, he
knighted his squire, and promised him to be my husband ;
and he hath pledged himself to give us four hundred
pounds' worth of land.   Here is the charter—yourself
may see."

When the lady had read the charter she was glad, but
she said only : " Hadst thou taken Sir Degrevant himself,
then hadst thou prospered well ! "

" Nay, madam, there is no lady alive whom he will wed
save you alone.   No emperor or king shall marry you—I
out-take none—but he shall prevent him !   He sends you
in greeting—behold—a red-gold ring set with a splendid
stone."

The lady saw that it was a royal gift : " This is a
marvellous thing !   Dost ween I be mad, to do such folly
as to love my father's foe, though he were ever so doughty ?
Nay, by the Rood !   I bid thee understand well, I will

have no husband yet a while—and so tell him when ye
meet.   Nay, more, I wish him no good !   The Duke of
Gerle has promised to sup here to-night; see that my
chamber be ready, and forget nothing."

Now is the duke come over the sea with a great following ; and the noble earl hath prayed him courteously to
dwell for ten days, at his cost for food, court, and wages of
knight, squire, and page.   And every evening one thousand and three horses belonging to the duke's meiny were
given their portions of corn and hay.

As the great duke sat at dinner, the earl readily promised him that he should have sweet maid Melidore to
wife.

Now this duke was so gay and amorous that the men of
the earl's house held him for a chivalrous knight ; and the
earl himself told what deeds of arms he had undertaken,
and how all his best men had been slain under the wood-
boughs.   " The banneret that dwells near by will assay
the jousting, he who wrought me all this damage and did
me this hurt."

The duke answered in haste : " Here I plight you my
word, whether he will tourney or fight, he shall have his
fill !   How shall I know him ? "

Then said the earl : " He bears in chief [1] azure figured
with a satyr under a double head-dress, and true-loves here
and there ; and on a background of black,[2] a lion tied to an

_____
[1] The upper third of a shield.   [2] See note.

oak in gold and green.   He wears a splendid helmet cleanly
cast into the form of a gold dolphin, with true-loves in the
border.   He is like a lion in the field, when he is ready
with his buckler, and his helmet is strongly plated, for it
stands like a stack.[1]   He is so stiff in battle, by St. Martin
of Tours, that if he could love as well, his peer could not
be found !   I would give all the lands I have to any knight
that would undertake to bring him down in the field ! "

The duke laughed him to scorn, and proudly swore an
oath : " Sir, he shall pay for all this to-morrow, for your
sake ! "

In the morning the duke busked him as fast as he might,
and so did the bold and cruel earl.   In the clear sunshine,
five hundred knights with their banners assembled, featly
armed, and their servants as well.   And all the broad
countryside came thither that day to see the sport.   Out
of the west[2] Sir Degrevant brought three hundred picked
knights graithed[3] all in green.

There was none so bold as to challenge the duke, who
proudly held the field ; but when they saw Sir Degrevant
come up armed, riding a Barbary horse, all the other side
thanked God for their chance.   Banneret and bachelor
drew near him to fight under his pennant in the tourney
that day.

With trumpet and drum and clear-sounding shawm
they rushed together, and when they met, many a bold

---

[1] Perhaps rock.   See note.   [2] See note.   [3] Clad.

knight was thrown by the way and lay stunned and fouled
under the horses' feet.   They smote mightily with their
swords, and soon many of these fierce fellows in their
armour had no longer any joy of life.   Barons were sitting
on the bent, shamefully hacked about the shoulders, and
with bleeding brows ; and many a man was hurt that never
assented to come to that tournament to do such deeds.

Sir Degrevant pricked fast through the press, and reached
the duke such a stroke that he tottered to the ground, so
that presently the knight won his black steed.   He was so
stalwart in that battle, for love of the lady who watched
from the tower, that, ere he stopped, he had won and
brought to the stake[1] sixty horses, as many a man saw.   To
tell the truth, he won that day the chief place in the jousting, having vanquished all the field ; and many stared at
him for his hardihood.   Fair ladies said one to another,
alike queen and countess, " Yonder knight in green hath
earned the prize ; " and they loved him well.

Presently the duke was horsed again, and pricked fast
through the field ; and he and the earl, with their following, went back to the castle ; and a herald cried upon all
the chivalry to come to the feast.

The good knight Sir Degrevant had made provision
for all his men, for forty days and more, so he withdrew to a
fair castle a little aside, near a fell,[2] and there made merry
and slew care.   Three hundred and more stern knights,

---

[1] Barrier in the lists ?   [2] Hill : North Country word.

who came out of that tournament, rode away in his company. One hundred pounds he sent, and a horse, to pay the minstrels ; he was never niggardly of his gifts, in weal or in woe. To this castle he rode, and held a royal feast ; and all his bold men stayed with him. At eventide, he said : " As I live, I will see the chivalry of France face to face ! "

So in the evening light he armed him at all points, and called to him two knights that were ever of his counsel.

" Busk ye on your steeds in the garments of damsels, for I must try my luck to-night. Take each of you a spear for peace or for war, and make ready my horses, and look they be trapped gaily with mantelets [1] and toptelers.[2]

Their horses were held for them, they took shield and spear and pricked fast over the plain, and rode straight westward through a fair forest, with two fine trumpets that rang out like bells.

On a hill the knight rested and donned his helmet, and without tarrying galloped to the earl's castle—the grimmest guest between heaven and hell ! He had the good hap to find the gate open wide, and so rode up to the very daïs where dinner was being served, and sought out maid Melidore, and greeted her.

As the duke started up, Degrevant said : " Here I plight thee my word, I shall deliver this bright lady to-

[1] Here, perhaps, *saddle-cloths*, or *foot-cloths*.
[2] Forehead ornaments ? See note.

morrow between prime and undern.   Look ye come then, or ye shall swoon away for sorrow before her eyes !   Truly, as I live, ye shall be served with three courses of war or of jousting ! " [1]

The knight was splendidly attired as was a joy to see ; and never before had they beheld so good a horseman. Some stared at his steed, some at his rich armour, and some took note of the cause that brought him thither. He bows to them, alike high and low, and busks him to ride out of the hall ; and of all that looked upon him none knew him save the fair maiden Melidore.

He rode homeward as fast as he might, and on the morrow he arrayed him as before, and found the duke in the field, with spear and buckler.   And the earl watched from a distance, as fierce as a boar.

Then said the duke : " Where is this giant ?   For all his great fare he will not keep his word ! "

But when he saw Sir Degrevant riding up on his Barbary steed, his heart grew faint within him and he groaned.   Being sore adread, he sent a squire to ask whether the knight would joust as in peace or in war, and he had an answer both reasonable and courteous : " It shall be as he will—chance what may ! "

Then these doughty men geared them fast, set on their helmets, chose two great spears of peace, and on their strong steeds pricked fast through the throng.   Their horses

[1] See note.

I.

rushed together, they jousted awhile ere they cast, and
then their good spears were all splintered.   Sir Degrevant,
as he had intended, gave the duke such a blow that, by my
hand, he lost both his stirrups !   But he recovered himself,
and thereby gladdened his friends, who gave him white
bread, Vernage, and wine of Crete.[1]   He swore by God in
heaven : " Would my steed but hold out, I would risk
anything for sweet Melidore ! "

They took two great spears that made their horses groan;
and so they rode through the ranks with many an eye upon
them, but that time they missed each other.   But at the
third course the knight Sir Anterous [2] came, strong in his
love, and pierced the duke's shield, as the earl saw from
afar, and grew heavy of heart.

The damsel [3] took the horse, and led him through the
ranks, saying : " Have this for thy reward till thou get
more."   But she added a proud word : " On this steed
shall I ride with my lover."

Again the knight geared him and took a sharp spear, a
weapon of war, from his fellow's hands,[4] to slay the duke,
while the lady said : " Sir duke, ye are proud; I pray
you keep your word.   Yonder is a knight-errant—why
tarry ye here ? "

[1] See list of wines in *The Squire of Low Degree*, with note on
p. 194 below.

[2] Evidently Degrevant.   See note.

[3] Melidore's maid ?   [4] His former squire's ?

But the duke lay stunned, and still she cried upon him :
" Yonder knight is all armed, and awaits you ! "

He answered as courteously as he could : " I may not
hide that I am hurt full ill. Pray him take no offence ;
he sees that I am wounded. I can scarce live, so sore
is my side ! "

Then Sir Degrevant gave his horse to pay the minstrels ;
and he and his men sped away to the forest. But the
duke, who had fared so ill, took his leave that same night,
and went home with all his barons.

On the morrow, Sir Degrevant came again to the thorn
where before he had left his steed ; and there all that day
he waited. At night he and his friend went secretly to try
if he might get speech with sweet Melidore.

The damsel knew by a token that they were come in, and
her lady perceived her thought : " Damsel, as I live, thou
hast got thee for guests again the wild men of the west—
hide it not ! Bring that knight here unseen to talk with
me in secret. By my word, he hath bought it dear ! "

Then the maiden was glad, and did her command, and
led him up the steps to her chamber. At the door stood
the noble lady herself, and there fell at his feet ; but quick
as fire struck from flint, he had caught her in his arms, and
kissed her thirty times ere he paused.

" Welcome, Sir Anterous, methinks thou art a wonder !
Wist the lord of this house, he would greet thee in all
wrath ! "

Presently were fetched chairs with velvet cushions, where these fair lovers might sit and kiss.

" Damsel, look there be a fire in the chimney of fir-faggots gathered long since."

The damsel set a board of ivory on trestles, and covered it with such cloths as never were seen before : Aylsham towels [1] as white as sea-foam, and surnapes [2] of the same. There was a golden salt-cellar, and basin, and ewer full of clear rose-water for their washing.

Secretly she brought white bread from the pantry, and served them as they sat. And she fetched from the kitchen a shield of wild boar, and haslets [3] in galantine, by my hand ! And they had plovers in pastry, fresh fat conies, pheasants and curlews, and all sorts of meats ; and she drew for them wine of Crete and Vernage. It were hard to tell all the dainty dishes and spices that were served at that meal; and still the maiden drew wine for him, Rochelle and Rhenish and Malmsey,[4] and filled his cup. And ever between, Melidore sat harping sweet notes, and sang merry songs ; and in that chamber of love they made such mirth that they slew care.

The roof of the room [5] was royally adorned with bright bezants,[6] and the wall was inlaid with white whalebone,[7]

---

[1] See note.
[2] Cloths to lay over the tablecloth for the washing of hands.
[3] Pig's fry.   [4] See note on p. 194.   [5] See note.
[6] Unstamped gold pieces like the coin.   [7] Walrus-ivory.

azure, and many a precious gem. There might be seen
archangels in red gold,[1] fifty together all laughing full
lightly ; the *Apocalypse* of John, Paul's *Epistles*, and the
Parables of Solomon w re there painted. And the four
Gospellers[2] sat on pillars, where listening to them were four
doctors, Austin[3] and Gregory, Jerome and Ambrose. All
the philosophers were portrayed in stone, and likewise
the story was there of unhappy Absalom. And there was
a clock on high to ring out with bells the hours of the
night and waken sweet Melidore. There were square
glass[4] windows the richest ever made, with little horns[1]
of hand-worked brass. All the walls were of agate,[1] with
high vaultings whereon were portrayed kings of far-away
lands on their thrones : Charles the Great with his crown,
Godfrey de Bouillon[1] and King Arthur of Britain, all with
their bright swords. The floor was tiled with clear
crystal, with a carpet of fine pall where the lady stood.

Her bed was of azure, with a tester and canopy bordered
with the story of Amadas and Ydoyne,[1] with precious
stones everywhere in a design of green popinjays.[1] And
there were, too, the scutcheons of many a knight, in gold
and cypress, with bright bezants and true-loves here and
there. No queen or empress had a more splendid bed, and
from her tester hung the king's own banner. There were
sheets of pure white silk, and quilts of the same, and
tasselled bags[1] with crystal knobs made in Westphalia[1] by

---

[1] See note.   [2] Evangelists.   [3] Augustine.
[4] Still uncommon at this time.

skilled women. It was marvellous to see the curtains hanging from many a ring of red gold ; and the cords that they ran on had been won by Duke Betys and spun by Melidore out of mermaidens' hair.[1]

About midnight Sir Degrevant asked : " When wilt thou listen to me, sweet lady ? My heart breaks with love ! When wilt thou set it at rest ? Lady, if it be thy will, be kind to me ! "

But she answered quickly : " No more of that, else shalt thou rue it bitterly ! Though thou be a knight, thou shalt get no love from me ere thou wed me with a ring. Believe me, the first time I met thee, my heart was so stirred that I thought never to have husband or lover save thee alone, kaiser or knight, king or conqueror, or lord of renown—not even the emperor himself. Therefore, sir, have patience till thou win my father's assent."

To that he agreed, and they plighted their troth, as glad and light-hearted as falcons on the wing. And there they rested together that night ; but, know well, it was without sin. The lady said to him : " Sweet sir, come every day, and see how we fare." So it was likewise with Melidore's damsel and her brave bachelor ; and this went on three-quarters of that year and more.

On midsummer night, the moon shone wondrous clear when Sir Degrevant and his knight busked them to go. As they dismounted by a tree, a forester saw them lingering

[1] See note.

in the glade, and followed them all the way through the wood until they had passed the stream. Likewise, the watchman on the wall, who was the earl's own minstrel, saw them turn towards the court, and wist never what it meant. The piper held his peace, and said nought to any man—minstrels should aye be courteous and excuse what they may! But the forester anon told the earl and his knights how these men came armed as he had seen.

Now the steward was a stalwart man, Sir Eymere the Kayous;[1] and with other fierce, bold officers of the house, he made a great bushment even where the forester had met Sir Degrevant, and thought to stop the green ways for him. The steward sware mightily: "An he come by this thorn, we shall take his head to-morrow, nor ask other reward!"

Dame Melidore wist not at all the intent of this folk, for she weened that no man knew of their meetings. And Sir Degrevant had promised on his honour to speak with her that night, and to stop for no fear.

> *God as Thou art mighty save the good knight,*
> *And lend him Thy grace to speed in that fight!*

At eventide he and his fellow armed them, and for fear of being discovered, put on green gowns. They had neither shield nor spear, nor any weapon of war save two keen Florentine swords.

[1] See note.

When they reached the ravine, an ambush of armed men on horses rushed out upon them. Sir Degrevant swiftly drew his sword, and he that came on first was soon slain in that shaw.[1]

When they all rushed together, seven spears set upon him and splintered a-two against his bacinet ; but some bore through his gown, and some split against his habergeon, while the second knight was overborne and his sword cast away from him. But Sir Degrevant at once dismounted and saved him, crying : " Why liest thou thus ? "

The best steeds they had he sliced through the shoulders; but never before, in weal or in woe, had he been so hard bestead. The steward, Sir Eymere, came a little too close, and his head was carved away at the collar. The body sat still upon the horse, an uncomely sight, as the steed leaped over a ditch and ran away. I know never how it went, but he beat them fast to the earth with such play of his two-handed sword that sixty were stretched on the earth with shield and spear, that might never wield weapon after that day. The earl's panter, his butler, and his chief squire lay dead together in that gay wood ; and the remnant fled from the doom they foresaw, but some lurked hidden under trees in the sloughs. Thanks be to God's grace, he hath vanquished his foes by his chivalry, and makes a bold chase and keen after those that are left. Not forty feet from the castle, he slays the marshal of the hall and more than fifteen good squires.

[1] Coppice.

By the time he had ended his sword-play, it was dawn, and but few had escaped, while many were slain.

Then said Sir Degrevant : " Here I promise thee that I will speak openly with Melidore to-night."

They left their steeds where they stood, passed the stream and went straight to the castle gates.

The sweet lady gave them fair welcome, for she had not heard of the fight ; whereof they were fain. But she was greatly a-wondered why their clothes were all torn as if they had been pierced by spear-thrusts in the woods ; and indeed their gay green gowns were shameful to look upon.

" Dear sir, where have ye been so to tear your clothes ? "

The knight sat down quietly and said to her aside : " It was no ferly thing that hurt us ; but only that we tore our gowns on a thorn as we came by. We shall have new to-morrow ; and we count this mishap not worth a pear."

He had fought like a wild boar and was greatly athirst, so the maid brought quickly wine and spices. They ate together divers sweetmeats and often kissed, and were served with Vernage and Cretan and Rhenish wine. At daybreak he took his leave of maid Melidore, who as yet wist naught of the fray ; that she was to hear after.

Sir Degrevant returned where lay the dead men, and said softly in his mirth, " Yonder was a stout hind ! "

They brought home on biers, Sir Eymere the steward and other good henchmen who had had enough of that frith; and thereupon there was a great outcry among all the folk in the castle, and Melidore went into the hall to ask tidings.

Says the earl to her : " Sir Degrevant and thee I blame for the loss of all my men ! That is thy treason ! By Him that perished on the Cross, thou shalt die to-day ! I wot well he hath dishonoured thee ! "

The maid answers : " Peter ! I am glad *he* is not slain ! Wherefore should I lie ? Since first I chose him for my mate, I will never forsake him, whatever dole or death I must endure ! "

Then the earl waxed mad and swore by bones and blood, " I will never taste meat or drink ere I see thee die ! "

The countess kneeled before him with shrill lament : " God forbid, sir, that she be slain, when we had never child but this ! Alas, ye have been foes too long ! Wicked tongues are the cause of it—God give them shame! I dare say this brave knight was going his ways when our men, through no fault of his, beset him. Were not his foresters killed while he was fighting in Spain, and his woods and warrens destroyed ? I counsel that ye make peace with him and give him Melidore in marriage."

Then said the maiden : " There was only himself and one other ; I spoke with him to-night—why should I not tell ? He is my lover and my lord, my hope and my comfort ; and it is good that ye make peace ! If ye continue to torment us, I will never touch food again ! "

The earl sweated for rage, but sighed at last : " Damsel, rather than that thou die, I forgive thee thy guilt. Have it thine own way—I can say no more."

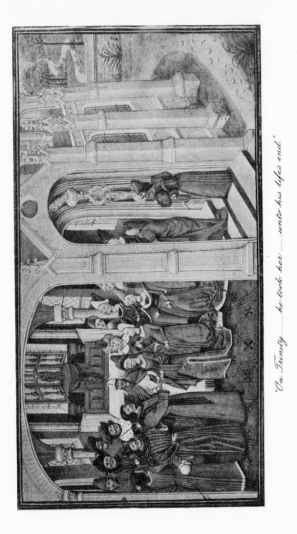

'On Trinity .... he took her .... unto his life's end.'

Belive at the earl's command, she sent a letter by messenger, with full new tidings. She bade Sir Degrevant come in secret with his best chivalry, as he was a good knight and doughty and leal, and she should make such accord between him and her father as should be of comfort to all that knew him ever. He was somewhat adread, but busked sixty knights, and at daybreak hastened to the earl's castle.

There the earl met him outside with stern and stalwart knights, and louted wonder low as he hailed him, saying : " Sir, by God's grace, we have been foes too long, and now will I be thy friend ! "

Then they talked aside, so that no man knew, until all wrongs were redressed ; and after, they kissed and went into the chamber. Not to rehearse at greater length, peace was made, and the earl granted the knight young Melidore until his life's end.

Never in France, nor yet in England before, was there such purveyance as at this wedding. Thither came an emperor and a king, and more than fifteen archbishops. The Mayor of the Hospital [1] came over with a cardinal, and the great King of Portyngale with bold knights. All the lords and ladies, alike empress and queen, of the land, were at that ceremony.

On Trinity, as the romance says, he took her according

[1] The head of the order of Knights Hospitallers, of which there were many foundations.

to the law of God, unto his life's end.   With all solemnity, a cardinal, invested with a pontifical ring, chanted the royal mass, and wedded that lady.   And the emperor gave her away at the kirk door with as much pomp and dignity as if she had been of his kin.   And along the ground where they had passed, glittered a thousand pounds' worth of gold.

Then assembled in the hall, the king and cardinal, the royal emperor, and bold barons and gay ladies, alike countess and queen—a joy to behold !   When the feast was served, wine ran in the conduit ready for each man who would take thereof ; and nine douzepers [1] of France took part in the dance.   Methought such an array a fair thing to see !

I know never a man who could describe the meats served in the hall ; and minstrels had great gifts of splendid robes and garments.   For each of fourteen days, there was a jousting of serried knights, and revelling with wine and ale ; and on the fifteenth day that noble company took leave and went home.   All praised, both knights and ladies, the courteous bearing of Sir Degrevant, who at that time gave away horses worth a thousand pounds, and also hawks and hounds and falcons.

That same year the earl died, and also his fair countess, and both had goodly burial.   And when Sir Degrevant fell heir to their broad lands, he might overmatch any peer in the country.   Thirty winters and more he and his

[1] The twelve knights of Charlemagne.

lady lived together in bliss, and had seven children. When she died he turned over the estate to his heir, and went to the Holy Land—may heaven be his meed! He was slain at Port Jaffa, jousting with a sultan; and thus this man of doughty deeds hath gone to his God.

> *Lord God in Trinity,*
> *Grant them Heaven for to see*
> *That love a story or a glee,*
> *And jesters for to feed!*

THE KNIGHT OF COURTESY AND FAIR LADY OF FAGUELL

> *In Faguell,[1] a fair countree,*
> *A great lord did sometime dwell,*
> *Which had a lady so fair and free*
> *That all men good of her did tell.*

SHE was fair and pleasant to look upon, gentle and amiable to men of all ranks, and as true to her husband as the turtle-dove on the tree. For her goodness and grace, she was loved alike by young and old.

There lived in that same land a brave knight, wise and full of prowess. Indeed, so much was his hardihood

---

[1] Faïel, near St. Quentin in Northern France.

spoken of by rich and poor, that he was called *The Noble Knight of Courtesy*.

Now this lord heard tell of the knight's good conditions, and sent to him a messenger with a letter, to say : " Sir, I pray you may one day see God ! My lord of Faguell by me sends you greeting an hundredfold, and bids you come anon to dwell at his court, where you shall lack no manner thing, nor town nor towered castle."

The courteous knight was content to go with the messenger to offer his service ; and they rode fast, day and night, until they were come thither, and were met by that lord and greeted with friendly welcome. So richly was he soon endowed with towns and towered castles that other men envied him, and thought by some treachery to rob him of his high estate.

Seeing him so good and true, the lady of whom I spoke before, set her heart and soul on him above all other men, and thought to be loved by him, nowise in sin but in chastity, even as children are kind one to another. And so likewise he loved her firm and fast in his heart and soul, sinlessly, but with a love that lasted till they died.

Day and night these true lovers suffered great pain, sorrow, and distress, because they might not reveal their hearts one to another, till at last, by a sudden chance, the knight was in a green garden, thus complaining mournfully : " Alas, now is my heart in woeful pangs ! I cannot refrain from lamentation, so doth love of this lady wound me! And me, I fear, she disdains!" And with that he threw himself on the ground.

Now the lady lay in a window, her heart as cold as any stone. She wist not what to do or say when she heard the knight's complaint. Sorely she sighed, and the colour fled her face. But when she came down into the garden where he lay on the ground, and when she saw him thus for her sake, her heart was almost broken for sorrow; and finding no comfort, she fell upon him in a swoon.

Presently the knight recovered, and when he saw her by his side took comfort, and began to cheer her, saying: " Lady-love, who hath brought you into this grief?"

And she: " My lover and my comfort, so your fairness standeth in my thought that, had I no mate in this world, none but yourself should ever have my heart!"

The knight said: " Lady, I shall in all honesty hold you dear, for your own sweet sake! Our love shall be none other, chaste and true and free from sin, than that which is between brother and sister. And wherever my body be, day or night, at all times my simple heart shall ever more abide with you, my lady!"

Then she, white as a flower and full of feminine shame-fastness, began to change her fair colour, saying to him: " Never doubt, my love, that in such wise shall I love you faithfully, next to God on high, alike in wealth and in adversity!"

They kissed each other in sign of troth; but even

then, alas! there was a foe behind the wall to espy them, who after turned all their joy to woe.

When they left the garden they parted; but their sorrowful laments were all past, for each had eased the other's heart.

Then the spy of whom I spoke, that had stood behind the wall, went boldly to his lord, and said : " Sir, I must tell you that, as I was walking by your garden, I heard the Knight of Courtesy talking secretly with your lady of unlawful love. Therefore, if you suffer him to proceed to have his joy of her, either he will be led away from you, or between them they will compass your end."

When the lord understood the spy's words, he swore that the knight should be driven from that land, were he never so strong and bold; and he vowed by Almighty God never to rejoice while that knight remained there, nor until by some means he should be slain.

He let cry a feast for all that would come thither, great or small; and there arrived many, old and young. The lord was set at the head of the table, and his lady by him; and the Knight of Courtesy was fetched and placed on the other side. The hearts of these lovers would have been woebegone, had they known what was in the lord's mind!

When they were all still, he spoke these words : " Methinks it is fitting for a knight to seek adventures, and not always to sojourn at home by the fire. Therefore, Sir Knight of Courtesy, I counsel you to go and ride through the country, seeking chances that may turn to your advantage, as to fight in Rhodes [1] and maintain the Christian faith, or show your strength by deeds of arms in Lombardy, Portugal, and Spain."

Then said the knight to that lord : " For your sake, and for my lady's, your dame's, I will risk my life, whether I ever return or no.   If I did not so, I were at fault."

At that word, the lady sighed, for her heart was ta'en with deep grief and pierced as by a sword.

After dinner, the knight went to make ready his horse and harness ; and this woeful lady came to him, and said right piteously : " Alas, if ye go, I must lament here alone, a creature full sorrowful ; and if ye be slain in battle, I may not endure to live !   Alas, unhappy woman ! Where shall I go ?   Where shall I bide ?   Now indeed am I sure of death, and shall set aside all earthly joy ! "

She took a pair of shears, and cut off her bright yellow hair.   " Wear this," she said, " on your helmet, for my sake, gentle knight."

" Dear lady, for your sake I will," the knight answered, with still mourning ; and finding no comfort, he could not but sigh heavily.

For great pity I cannot write of the sorrow that was between those two ; and my respite for labour [2] is all too short to tell of their pain and sorrow.   No man could ever depaint the sad parting and lamentation of these lovers

[1] See note.   [2] My working-time.

I.

twain, so bitterly they grieved. For very dolour, tears ran from their eyes as they said farewell.

The lady remained in her castle, her heart ever replenished with languor ; and there let us leave her making moan, and turn to the courteous knight, who has gone forth on his journey.

He said unto himself : " I will not fight against Christians, but will go to Rhodes, there to sustain them with all my might."

Then he unfolded her hair and set it high on his helmet, with red threads of rich gold that she had given him. His shield was wrought splendidly with azure and beaten gold ; but he thought on nothing but herself when he beheld her yellow hair.

Eager for battle, he rode forth by dale and down, to seek adventures in many a town, city, and castle. In every jousting where he came, none was found so good as himself ; and in every place he smote his adversary to the ground and won the prize.

When he came into Lombardy, there was a dragon in the neighbourhood, who did great hurt and damage to man and beast. As the knight rode alone, with only his page by his side, he began to bemoan his love with bitter sighs : " Alas, my sweet lady ! God wot in what case ye be ! God wot when we shall see each other again—I fear me never ! " Then, as he looked towards a high hill, he heard a shout of the dragon, and said : "Yonder is a feast

indeed ! " He blessed him and rode forward, saying :
" I shall do my part. Betide me weal or woe, I shall
assail this fierce monster ! "

With this, he met the dragon, and she, seeing him, gaped
wide; but he took good heed, and started a little away, and,
drawing his sword like a knight to attack her, gave her
mighty strokes, so that the battle was strong and deadly.

The dragon wounded the knight on the head with her
tail, so that he fell a-swoon like a dead man ; but quickly
he arose, and with a prayer to God and Our Lady to help
him in that fight, started with fierce courage up to the
dragon, and so watched for his advantage that he smote off
her tail. She began to yell, and turned upon her side ;
and quickly on the alert, he let his sword slip into her body
so that she could scarce move. Seeing this, he drew near
and lightly smote off her head, and so escaped that danger.
Straightway he thanked God of His grace, who by virtue
of His Deity, and by His goodness and mercy, had preserved him at that time.

He went to a nunnery there beside, where a surgeon
with skilful art healed his wide wounds. And after, he
departed thence toward the Rhodes, to fight in battle as he
had undertaken to do, and to sustain the faith with all his
might ; for he would not break his pledge.

At that time there was a rout of Saracens, all armed and
in array, besieging Rhodes fiercely towards Good Friday.[1]

[1] See note.

Hence, the knight was welcomed by all within the city, and anon they provided him with battle.

So for the time I leave them there, and return to the bright lady who dwelled at home with sorrowful face. Day and night she mourned, crying: " Alas, my love is gone away! Alas, my gentle knight, my heart is sore for thy sake! If only I might see thee once afore my death, I ask no other thing! Alas, what treason or envy hath made him go from me? I think my own lord in anger hath traitorously done him to death! Alas, my lord, ye were to blame thus to betray my love! It is right great shame to you, since our love was pure always, and we never intended sin! Alas, gentle being! Wherever thou goest, love, wherever thou ridest, never shalt thou be out of my mind! Ah, Death, where art thou so long from me? Come and part me from my sorrow; for till I be dead and buried, I can never cease lamenting! Farewell, dear love, wherever thou art! For thy sake, joy is gone from me; and till such time as I see thee again, I must still mourn uncomforted! "

Thus complained this clear-faced lady, grieving alone; and nothing could cheer her or give her ease, so was she oppressed with woe and pain.

So let us leave her in this state, ever bewailing her lover; and let us turn again to the knight at Rhodes. When the day of battle was come, the Christians all armed them, and went out of the city to fight strongly against God's foes.

It was a seemly sight to see them ready for war, many a doughty man come from afar to that battle.

The Knight of Courtesy entered the field, well armed and riding fast ; and both knights and barons beheld that none was better geared than he. His helmet was set with many a precious stone, and above was the comely hair as red as gold.

The trumpets sounded, the spears rushed together and broke the array ; and with great noise of guns,[1] in an encounter not playful, on every side was joined fierce battle. The Knight of Courtesy was not slow to smite down all that awaited him ; and his match could nowhere be found.

There was a strong and doughty Saracen who envied him, and ran at him with all his might, saying : " Traitor, I defy thee ! "

They rushed together with long spears, and anon the Saracen lay on the ground, and the knight drew his sword and smote off the head.

There came ten other Saracens in a rout, and so strongly assailed and beset him on all sides that fierce battle began again. Presently he cast four to the ground with four strokes ; but the others multiplied still, and gave him many a hurt. They laid on him from every side cruel strokes and deadly, and pierced him with such deep, wide wounds that he fell to the earth.

Then the Saracens went away and let him lie—a piteous

[1] See note.

sight !—with mortal wounds. Anon he called his page
and said : " My time is come. In my heart is so deep a
wound that, without gainsaying, I must die. But ere ye
bury me in the ground, I pray thee one thing : cut my
heart out of my body, and wrap it in this yellow hair ; and
when ye depart hence, convey it to my lady. Promise me
without delay to take it to her as a present, and bury my
body in the cross-ways."

The page was right sorrowful and dolent, but as soon
as the knight had yielded up the ghost, he buried his
master as he had been commanded, and went towards
Faguell with the heart and the hair. Sometimes he
walked and again he ran, with woeful lament and sorry jest,
until he came into the forest near the castle of Faguell.

Now the lord of Faguell was in the wood with his meiny,
and presently met the page and asked : " Boy, what tidings
with thee ? How is the case with thy master ? Tell me
truly ere thou goest, or thou shalt never leave this place ! "

Thereupon the page was afeared, and sad at heart, and
gave up to the lord the heart and also the hair. He told
him the truth of the whole matter : how the knight was
slain in battle, and had sent the lady that thing for a
special token of love.

The lord took good heed, gazing upon the heart, that
high present, and said : " Their love was hot indeed ; and
they lived in great torment."

Then he went home and into the kitchen. " Cook," he

said, " listen to me. Dress me anon this heart [1] in the daintiest wise that may be. Make it sweet and delicate to the taste. It is for my lady, who would not be the merrier if she wist what the meat were." And he said again that such food was doleful and deadly ; and so the lady found it when she knew.

Presently the lord went into the hall, and was set at meat, and his lady near him ; and he bade the heart to be fetched—whereof proceeded great woe.

" Madam," he said, " eat of this, for it is dainteous and pleasant." And the lady did so, undismayed, for there was no lack of good spices.

And when she had done, her lord said to her : " You have eaten, every deal, the heart of him to whom you gave your yellow hair. Of a surety, your knight is dead, and ye have eaten his very heart. Madam, at the last, we must all die."

Hearing this, the lady cried : " My heart will break for woe ! Alas, that ever I saw this day ! Now may my life last no longer ! "

She rose in parlous estate, and went straight to her chamber, when she confessed her devoutly, and soon after received the Sacrament. Then she laid her grieving on her bed—God wot, woeful was her lament ! " Alas ! " she cried, " mine own dear love, since thou art dead, my joy is done ! Have I indeed eaten thy heart ? That meat

[1] See note.

shall cost me dear ! Now, alas, must I die of grief ! Ah, noble, peerless knight, thy heart shall certainly die with me ! Thereon have I taken the Sacrament, and hereafter I refuse all earthly food. For woe and pain my life is spent! My cruel husband, why have ye done this cursed deed ? In slaying him ye have slain me also, and may the high God grant you your meed for this ! "

Then said her husband : " My fair lady, forgive me if I have misdone ! I repent me that I did not know ye would take this to heart so deeply ! "

The lady answered : " I forgive you. Adieu, my lord, for evermore. My time is come, and I may live no longer."

And he : " I am woe for that ! "

Great was the sorrow of all the lords and ladies of every degree ; some swooned, and all were full of grief for her death. Piteous it was to hear her complaint : " Adieu, my lord, now must we part. I die, husband, as true a wife as ever was found in Faguell. I never sinned with the Knight of Courtesy ; and we are woefully brought to confusion ! My lord, ye were to blame to make me eat his heart ; but sith I have so done, I shall never touch other meat ! Thereupon I have received the Eternal Food, and I shall never eat in earthly wise again. Now Jesus, that was slain on the Rood, have mercy on me, my life is done!"

> With that, the lady, in all their sight,
>   Yielded up her spirit, making her moan ;
> May God on high, greatest of might,
>   On her have mercy, and us each one !

THE SQUIRE OF LOW DEGREE

It was a squire of low degree,
That loved the king's daughter of Hungary.

SEVEN years he had served the king as marshal in hall to place all the lords according to their rank ; and so was he courteous and good, that every man loved him as his friend. Withal, he was brave and stout in battle ; but he mourned ever, none knew wherefore. And it was all for that lady, the king's daughter of Hungary. No creature in Christendom knew how well he had loved her for more than seven years ; and this was to no end, seeing that, although he was a gentleman, he was not rich of gold and goods.

He durst not make moan to any save himself alone, but ever when his sorrow pressed upon him, he would pass through his chamber out into a gay garden. There was a beautiful green arbour of the fairest trees [1] and plants in the world—of cypress, first chosen by Jesus,[1] of southern-wood and sycamore, red rose and lily, box and beech and laurel, date and damson and drooping filbert, fig-tree and round maple, peony, poplar and broad-branching plane, and many another tree and shrub.

On every bough perched three birds [1] singing melodi-ously : the laverock, red-breast and nightingale, the wit-wall, peacock and popinjay, the throstle piping all the

[1] See note.
153

while, the merle, the wren, and the swallow whipping to
and fro, the jangling jay and the mirthful lark, the sparrow
fluttering on her twig, the cheerful mavis, the nuthake
with her fresh notes, the starling with her true notes, the
goldfinch chirping gaily on a briar, and many other birds
that with their clear whistling brought comfort.   Always
when he was sorrowful, he would go into that arbour and
lay him down in the bent, right under her chamber window, with his back to a thorn-tree, crying : " Alas that
ever I was born !   Would I were rich in gold or lands or
other possessions, that so I might wed that sweet flower-
lady !   Or that I were come of gentle kin to win her love !
Would I were a king's son to woo her !   Or that I were as
bold in battle as the knight Sir Libius,[1] or as chivalrous as
Sir Gawain [2] or Sir Guy,[3] or as doughty of my hand as
the giant Colbrand ! [3]   If it were put in jeopardy what
man should win that sweet lady, the king's daughter of
Hungary, none should have her but I ! "   And ever he
cried : " Wellaway, poverty robs me of all my joy ! "

Now the lady heard this lament right under her chamber
wall, as she sat in her oriel that was enclosed in painted
glass, every window with a device and adorned with
tracery.   Quickly she undid an ivory bar, and flung the
casement wide, so that the sun streamed into her closet.

She beheld where the squire lay in that gay arbour, and

[1] See p. 165 below, with note on p. 194.
[2] See note on *Launfal Miles*, p. 183.   [3] See note.

called to him : " Sir, wherefore such moan ? Why
mournest thou, day and night ? Tell me now, squire, I
prithee ; and as I am a true lady, I will never make thy
counsel known, but save thou be to blame, I will help
thee in thy trouble."

Often had he been in joy and sorrow, but never before
so well as then. He fell on his knee, saying : " Lady, it is
all for you ! These seven years have I loved you, and
paid dearly for my love ! Ye are so rich of array, that I
durst never speak word of it to you, and of so high kindred
that I knew not how to begin. If I had told my will, and
ye had not been pleased, ye would have betrayed me to the
king, and brought me full soon to my death. And so,
fair, sweet lady, I durst never show my heart. But now I
am here at your will, to spare or slay ; and one word from
you might comfort me for all the sorrow I have had. If
ye will not do so, I must needs depart from this country,
and forsake my kindred, and become an hermit [1] in some
uncouth [2] place, begging my bread in many a land, and
seeking to find where Christ lived and died. I will make
me a staff of my spear, and will wear no linen, but wend ever
in travail until I come to the world's end ; and lady, but
ye be my help, no shoe shall ever touch my foot. O lady,
I prithee, by Him that died on Good Friday, put me not
to this peril for His love that harrowed Hell ! "

Then that lady from her oriel said right sweetly : " By

---

[1] He means *pilgrim*.   [2] Unknown ; hence, foreign.

Him that died on the Tree, I will not deceive you, squire;
and though I should be slain for your sake, I will return
your love ! Go forth and serve the king my father, and
lay aside all your secret mourning. Let no man know ye
were here alone in my arbour ; and as ye would fain have
your will, listen, and look, and hold your peace. Beware
of the steward, I pray you ; he will deceive you if he can.
If ever he wist of your wooing, he would betray you to the
king ; and anon ye would be taken and put into prison for
my sake. Then must ye needs abide the law, peradventure
to be hanged and drawn. Not for all the gold in Christendom would I see you thus ! But if ye would win my love,
ye must undertake chivalry and deeds of arms, by which ye
shall earn your shoon ; [1] and ye must ride through many a
perilous place as a venturous man for his lady's favour, [2]
over hills and dales and high mountains, in wet weather,
alike hail and rain ; and if ye find no harbourage, then must
ye lodge under a tree among wild beasts or tame—and so
shall you win renown. And ye must lie in your armour
every night for a while, and also your men, until seven
years be come and gone ; and for my love, squire, ye must
cross many a perilous sea. Wherever war awakens, ye must
enter upon battle, in every city throughout the land of
Lombardy. But be ye well advised when ye undertake a

[1] Spurs.
[2] So Chaucer's Squire : " In hope to stonden in his lady
grace."

combat, that ye stand ever in the right, and bearing this
in mind ye shall speed the better.   And when the war is
ended, ye shall journey to the Rhodes, and there fight on
three Good Fridays,[1] if ye would have praise of me.   Only
if ye overpass these three battles, are ye worthy to be a
knight and to bear arms of gold and gules set with sable.[1]
And ye shall have a blue shield in token of constancy, inlaid on both sides with golden vines, full of imagery, and all
besprinkled with true-loves!   Amid your shield shall be
set a lady's head in fretwork, and above it, for love of me,
the motto AMOR.[1]   The baldric[2] on which it hangs shall
be white with a red cross in token of the Trinity.[1]   Your
helmet shall be well burnished, your ventail[3] neatly fitted,
set with gold stars and covered with fine velvet, with a new
head-piece[4] and divers-coloured ostrich-feathers.   The
plates clasping your body shall sit seemly about the waist,
and your coat-armour[5] shall be of pure gold bordered
with rich ermine.

    " Thus, with six good yeomen by your side, shall ye ride
forth to your wars ; and when these be ended, it shall be-
hove you to journey farther, over many a perilous flood,
past fields and paddocks and dense forests, till you come to
Jerusalem to seek out where Christ lived and died.   There

---

[1] See note.   [2] Sword-belt, usually worn over one shoulder.
[3] Part of helmet left open for breathing.
[4] Helmet usually ; here, perhaps, crest.
[5] Tunic worn over armour.

must ye draw your battle-sword and bear it to the Sepulchre,[1] and among all the lords lay it on the stone, and offer five florins as long as ye live, and three more in token of the Trinity. When, sir, ye have done all this, then are ye worthy to wear your shoon, and ye may say justly that ye are proved a venturous knight. And I shall give you a thousand pounds to your spending when ye ride forth— that and a horse and armour—whereby ye may win honour and be greater than all your kith. I pray God and Our Lady send you the Wheel of Victory,[1] that my father may be fain to wed me to you and make you king of this country, to have and hold in honour, to wear the crown with wealth and prosperity, and to be lord of town and tower, that so we may live out our days in perfect, pure love. If we may not come to this, we must do otherwise ; but therefore, squire, go your ways, take leave of the king and queen and all the court, and hasten on your journey. And in your going you shall lack neither gold nor silver, nor anything else. Seven years I shall wait for you, betide what betide. Till seven years be come and gone, I shall remain unwed."

The squire kneeled down to thank that fair lady ; and kissing her thrice, he took leave and went his way.

But the king's steward stood in a chamber fast by, and heard all these words plainly—every deal of the wooing ; and he vowed to the King of Heaven that he would betray

[1] See note.

"The Wheel of Victory."

that sweet maid, and would have the squire taken and hanged high on a tree. The traitor was full of rage and longing to undo them, and bethought him daily how he might be revenged on that fair lady, in that he loved her secretly and was jealous of her. Alack, as soon as he was of their counsel, all their joy was turned to woe!

Now when the squire had parted from his gentle lady, he went to his chamber and arrayed him in scarlet-red with a broad-barred girdle, a chaplet on his hair and a horn about his neck; and thus he went forth to do his office in the hall, among the lords of high and low degree.

With a white rod in his hand, he went to kneel before the king, and served him right royally with dainty meats,[1] partridge, plover and peacock, and birds baked in bread, teal, duck and drake, cock, curlew and crane, pheasant, stork, snipe, and fresh venison of buck and doe, and many other dainties fit to set before a king.

And when the squire had so done, he served to and fro in the hall, honoured and loved by men of every degree. The king beheld him in his fair raiment, and thought him the comeliest man that he had seen in the world ever; and with that, all at once he loved him, though he wist never wherefore or why.

Thus he sat still, and ate right naught for thinking of his squire. Of this the steward took good heed, and came and told the king all he had heard of the wooing: how she had

1 See note.

promised him land and goods, and great plenty of gold and silver; and how he was to take his leave and become a knight for her sake: " And thus, while they talked together, I drew me near and evermore near; and, had I not come in, verily the squire had dishonoured her. But when he perceived me, he fled fast away. On the truth of this, here is my hand. I will fight him to the death!"

Then the king said to the steward: " I cannot believe it should be thus. He hath been so debonaire and gentle, and hath served me since he was young,[1] aye ready and true of word and deed—I cannot believe he would betray my dear daughter, or tempt her to folly! And even though she consented, I trust him so fearlessly that I know he would never win her save in wedlock; and if this is her doing, he deserves no ill on that account. I have seen many a page who became a man by marriage; and so it is seemly that the squire should win my daughter in this manner. A man of any degree may become a prince by fortune or some other grace, by purchase[2] if not by heritage. Therefore, steward, beware and defame him not through envy. It were great pity he should be undone and put to death guiltless, and a heavy sorrow to my dear daughter. I would not for my new crown that she should lose her fair colour! So have a care unless thou take him in the deed, for if it be found that thou defame them through enmity, thou shalt be seized as a felon and put full deep in

---

[1] See note.
[2] Any lawful means of acquisition except inheritance.

prison and fettered fast to a stone till twelve years be passed, and then drawn by a horse through the city and hanged upon a tree !   And thou may not excuse thyself or deny this deed ;   therefore, steward, beware how thou shalt answer for it ! "

Said the steward, full of malice : " What I have said I will stand by, even to the suffering of death and endless woe !   Sire, I will never go back on this, and if ye will give me power and a force of men, I shall this very night take him in your daughter's chamber.   I shall never be content until I be avenged on him ! "

Then the king answered courteously : " Thou shalt have force enough, thirty-three men-at-arms, to watch over that lady and keep her from her enemies.   For there is no knight in Christendom but if he should betray her, he should die under his shield if ever I should come face to face with him !   Give heed to my words, steward, I prithee.   If the squire come to-night to speak with my daughter, let him say whatso he will; listen and watch and hold thy peace, and hearken well to his words, ere thou make any fray with him ;   and so he come not within her chamber, begin no quarrel, even though he kiss her at leave-taking, but let him go, whole and sound, without any wound or hurt.   But if he will break into her chamber, speak never a word, and even if he be come with company to her undoing, look he be taken anon and all his meiny, and brought by force into my prison as a traitor, thief, and

I.

false felon ; and if he make any defence, hew him as small as flesh that goes into the pot. If, on the other hand, he yield, bring him to me, safe and sound, and I will find surety that he shall not wed my daughter for seven years. Therefore, steward, watch that lady, night and day, I prithee."

The steward answered, " I will do your bidding," and took his leave to go.

The squire came down from his chamber into the hall, and summoned all the officers,[1] usher, panter, butler, and others, and bade them take up the tables ; and they did as he commanded. After, he himself went to the king and set him humbly on his knee, and cleared the board full decorously. And when he had so done, he said to the king : " As ye are a chivalrous lord, give me leave to pass the sea, to prove the strength of my right hand on God's enemies in a strange country, and to become known for my deeds in Gascony, Spain, and Lombardy, fighting all battles that I may be proved a venturous knight."

Said the king : " Thou shalt have leave to go. I will give thee gold and goods and a force of men. If thou be true in word and deed, I will help thee in trouble."

Upon this the squire gave him thanks, and took leave and rode forth, proud and joyful, with his meiny. But he had ridden only a little way, scarce a mile, ere he came to a

[1] See note.

village, and said to a page of his : " Look that our supper
be ready soon, for we shall lodge here to-night."

They took their inns thereupon, and presently went to
supper.   But when the squire was set and served at meat,
he said that he had forgotten to take leave of that noble
lady, the king's daughter of Hungary.   So he rose anon,
and went forth without his men, and returned to the
castle.

When he came to the postern-gate, he entered with
drawn sword, being alone ; and yet was he full hard bestead by the steward, as ye shall hear.   He thought that
none in the world knew his secret ; but alas, it was not as he
deemed !   For the steward was of his counsel and had betrayed him to the king, and now lay by the lady's chamber,
and beset it all round about with a great company of
armed men.   Treason walketh wonder wide !

The squire had no mistrust, but by St. John, had he
known what was toward, he had not come there alone.
Or if that lady had but wist his purpose, she would have
given him gold and goods and a right royal force of men ;
but none knew whither he departed when he went forth
alone from among his servants.

When he came to her chamber, he cried : " Undo your
door ; undo, my dear !   I am beset by many a spy !   O
my white [1] lady, there are thirty to my one !   Open your
door, sweet love ; I am threatened by many a knife !

[1] Text: *white as ivory.*

Undo, sweetheart ; there are strong foes all about me !
Lady, save ye arise, I am but dead through them ! Undo
your door, my lovely flower, as ye are mine and I am
yours ! "

At this the lady awoke, and, casting upon her a golden
mantle, cried out : " Go away, villain, you shall not come
here to-night ! I will not undo my door for any man that
comes to it ! There is but one in Christendom that ever
made foreward with me so that I promised to be his wife ;
and by sweet Mary, he shall wed me only when he is proven
a venturous knight. We have loved these seven years ;
and although kings and chevaliers, dukes and powerful
earls wait on me, I hold no other love so dear as his !
Therefore, squire, depart, for here ye get no prey. I wot
not who ye should be that thus beseech me of love ! "

" I am your own squire," he said.   " Be not dismayed
for me, lady ; I am come secretly to take my leave of you."

" Welcome," she cried, " dear my love ! Mine own
dear heart ! My squire ! I shall give you kisses three,
and a thousand pounds as a gift ; but I shall keep my
maidenhood till ye be proved a venturous knight. For if
ye should wed me now, my father would banish you anon ;
and though ye love me never so sore, ye shall not be slain
for my sake ! Go forth and ask me of my kindred, and
look what answer ye get ; if, i' fay, ye are granted, myself
shall not deny you.   But if ye may not do so, ye shall come
to it otherwise. Ye are hardy, strong, and bold—go forth

and be a venturous knight ; and I pray God and Our Lady
send you the Wheel of Victory, that my father may be lief
to proffer me to you. I know it is said lightly, ' Go forth,
and be not afraid.'   A man of honour may not do so, but
must have what he needs of gold and goods, and a strong
force of men ; so spare ye not gold or silver till your manhood be proven.   Into whatso battle ye enter, ye shall
have an hundred pounds, or two.   And if ye should say to
me that I would fain have you gone, and have offered you
gold and goods to be out of my sight, believe me, sir, it is
not so, but only for the honour of us both.   Though ye be
come of simple folk, yet ye may win my love if ye have as
much grace of victory as had ever Sir Guy,[1] or Sir Libius,[1]
when the dwarf and the maid Ely came to worshipful King
Arthur, so that he became a famous knight and won the
Lady of Synadowne ; for he was granted the battle,
although the dwarf was vexed and said :—

> ' *Arthur, thou art to blame !*
> *Bid this child go suck his dame.*
> *Better it seems him, as may I thrive,*
> *Than for to do these battles five !* '

At the chapel of Salebraunce, these words caused a great
tumult ; but when they saw he had the victory, they
kneeled down and cried his mercy ; and afterward, sir,
they called him the Knight Absolute, with emperors,

[1] See note.

dukes, knights, and queen to be at his commandment. Now may such fortune by grace betide you, to win the worthiest within the wall, and still think on your love alone, and change not."

Right as they talked together, their foes drew nearer and nearer. Four and thirty with glittering weapons had the steward arrayed for that fight, being ordained to spy and take them utterly.

The squire thought that he must go to his death, and felled seven men that set upon him at once. When he had brought these to the ground, the steward himself turned fiercely against him, and so hard they smote together that the squire smote the steward's throat a-two; whereupon he fell down mortally wounded, and died as a false traitor.

Then presently the other men caught the squire in their arms, and tore off his fine raiment and put it on the steward; and with their swords so hacked his face that the lady might not know who he was. And so they cast him, this steward stiff and stout, at her chamber door.

When they had done with that great affray, they stole away secretly with the squire unhurt, and so took him into the chamber of the king, who said : " Welcome, son. Ye thought to be my son indeed, but for seven years I will prevent you ! "

Let us leave the bold squire and return to the fair lady at her chamber door. " Alas ! " she cried. " Wellaway ! I have lain too long ! Alas, and all for woe ! Why camest thou so without men ?   If I had but known thy intent, I might have warned thee !   Too dearly have I paid for my love, but it shall not be lost utterly ! "

She took him in her arms and dragged him into the chamber, and there drew forth his bowels and buried them according to the law of God ; but the body itself she dried with spicery, with virgin wax and cummin, and enclosed it in a chest of maple-wood under three locks.   And this she put in a marble-stone and set at her bed's head, and every day she kissed him.   As soon as she arose in the morning, she would kneel down and make her prayer to the Trinity, and then kiss that body twice or thrice ; and ever when she had so done, would she swoon away.   Then would she go to the church and hear the five Masses which she had offered for as long as she should live.   " And none but the King of Heaven shall know for whom I make this offering."

Said the king : " My daughter, why are you so mournful—so fair and comely a lady as ye are ?   Ye were once ivory-white, and are now as grey as any stone ; ye were once red as a cherry, with arch brows and laughing eyes. Ye were wont to harp and sing, and to be the blithest in the chamber.   Once ye wore gold and good velvet, and damask-cloth set with sapphires.   Ye had gems on your head, red and white stones of the Orient, and gold coronals, with many a row of diamonds.   And now ye wear black garments—tell me, daughter, for whose sake ?   If he be so poor of renown that for shame ye may not be wedded, bring him to me, and straightway I will make him a squire or a knight ; and if he be so great a lord that ye may not grant him your love, let me but see him, daughter, and he shall have gold enow with thee."

" Gramercy, father, as I hope to thrive, I mourn for no living man ! And none, by the King of Heaven, shall know more of my sorrow ! "

Now the king understood it, every deal, but he kept his own counsel, and said : " To-morrow ye shall go a-hunt-ing, my dear, and ride in a carriage covered with red velvet, with hangings of bright gold about your head, with white damask and blue azure worked with fresh lilies. Your pommels [1] shall be tipped with gold, your chains richly enamelled, your mantle of splendid purple pall and ermine. And your carriage shall have sprightly jennets of Spain, with trappings to the ground of gay velvet. Ye shall have harp, psaltery and song, and other mirthful devices. And ye shall have Romney [2] and Malmsey, Hippocras and Vernage, Mount Rose and Greek wine, Algrade and Respice, Antioch and Bastard, Pyment and Granada, Muscadel, Claret, and Rochelle, the red to digest your stomach, and pots of Osey to set by you. Ye shall have baked venison, the best wild-fowl that may be caught, a leash of greyhounds to run with you after hart and hind and other such. Ye shall be set at such a

[1] Here, doubtless, of the saddles.   [2] See note on these wines.

trysting that the deer shall come to your hand.   To drive
away your misease, you shall hear the bugles blow and
watch the beagles and seven-score sleuthhounds in their
tracking.

" And ye shall ride homeward a-hawking by the river,
with goshawk and gentle falcon, with eaglehorn [1] and
merlin.[1]

" When you come home among your people, ye shall
have revels, dances, and songs ; and little children shall
sing for you like nightingales.

" Your evensong shall be of tenors and trebles, three
score, clad in capes of gay damask set with pearls.   Your
altar-cloths shall be of taffeta, your robes of the same silk.[2]
Your censers shall be of gold richly enamelled with azure.
Your choir and your organ shall give forth song, with
counternote and descant,[2] half of them playing on organs,
and with young children singing sweetly.

" Afterward, ye shall go to your supper, and sit in a tent
in a green arbour, decked to the ground with Arras [2] cloth
set with sapphires and diamonds.   On your head you shall
wear cloth of gold adorned with popinjays in red stones.
And you shall have officers at your bidding to bring you all
manner delights.   The nightingale sitting on a thorn shall
sing to you all the while.   An hundred knights told off for
the sport shall play at bowls [2] in cool alleys to drive away
your misease ; and you shall watch the fishes jumping in

[1] Other kinds of hawks.   [2] See note.

the pools, and walk up and down the arbour to see the
lovely flowers.

"Presently ye shall go to a drawbridge, half of stone and
half of wood ; and a barge [1] shall meet you with four-and-
twenty oars, with trumpets and clarions, to row up and
down the fresh water. And ere ye come home, ye shall go
out in the salt foam to look upon your manors ; and there
shall be with you eighty high-towered ships, splendid
dromedaries [2] and carracks [3] with two sails, the swiftest
that go on the water, with good galleys lying in the haven,
with eighty oars at their prows. And your mariners as
they row shall sing : ' Hey, how and rumbylowe ! ' [1]

"Then, daughter, ye shall call for wine with good rich
spices, pretty pots of green ginger, dates, and other
dainties. Forty gleaming torches shall give you light at
every bridge. And at last you shall be led to your
chamber with much mirth and joyance.

There your costards [1] shall be covered with white and
blue worked with fresh lilies, your curtains of draped
camaca,[4] your bed-posts [1] all of gold, with splendid gem-
work by your head. Your curtains shall be figured with
red and white popinjays, your coverlets furred with
ermine, and powdered with gold of fine hue ; your blankets
shall be of fustian, your sheets of Rennes cloth, your head-
sheet decked with gems, diamonds, and bright rubies.

---

[1] See note.   [2] Heavy ships, galleons.   Properly *dromonds*.
Light, swift-sailing ships.   [4] A kind of silk.

" When you are laid softly in bed, a golden cage shall be hung aloft, with long-pepper [1] burning and sweet-scented cloves, frankincense, and olibanum,[2] so that even while ye sleep, ye shall savour them. And if ye cannot rest, all night long minstrels shall wake for you."

" Gramercy, father, as I live, none of these things liketh me ! "

She passed into her chamber, and there fell a-swooning ; and so with deep sorrow and bitter sighs she kept that body seven years.

But now let us leave her and tell of the squire that was put in prison for her sake. Upon a day, the king himself went secretly and took him out and made him swear never to reveal what had befallen. And there the squire held up his hand never to gainsay the king's bidding ; and the king granted him leave to go forth on his journey, and in a word, to pass the sea so that no man wist save they two. And when he had done his wandering, he should return. " And thou shalt be in my chamber as I shall ordain for thee. And then shalt thou wed my dear daughter, and have my lands, both far and near."

At this the squire was full merry, and thanked the king and went his way, the king giving him both land and goods. Anon he passed the sea into Tuscany and Lombardy, where he wrought chivalrous deeds. In Portugal

---

[1] See note.
[2] An aromatic gum found in Africa and in India.

and in Spain no man might stand against him, and where-soever he went he bore away honour. Thus he travelled for seven years in many a land, near and far, till on a day he bethought him to go to the Sepulchre, and there he made his offering right as the king's daughter bade him.

Then presently he remembered him what the king had said, took leave of Lombardy, and rode home to Hungary; so came to the king as he before had made covenant to do. He told of the battles he had won and of the chivalrous deeds he had wrought in Lombardy; and the king was so pleased with these good tidings that he took him by the hand and made him full royal cheer, and said: " Wel-come, my dear son! Let none of thy meiny know thou art out of prison; but hold thee still in thy chamber until I learn my daughter's will."

So the king went alone under his daughter's window, where he might hear her moaning and learn her thoughts. Had the sweet lady wist he was there, he had not known so much of her mind. But she weened nothing of him when she began to weep and wail over that body, and cried: " Alas, that we must be parted a-two! " Twice or thrice she kissed it, and swooned away. " Alas! " then said the dear lady, " seven years have I kept thee, and now thou art turned to dust! No longer may I keep thee, dear love, but must render thee to the earth, with reading and sing-ing of priests. If any man ask what I have here, I will say it is my treasure; and if any would know why I keep it, I

will tell him, so it be safe from thieves.   For thy sake, O
my squire, I say fie on the vanity of this world !   Farewell, pure gold and fine, velvet and satin, castles and
manors ;   farewell hunting and hawking, revel, mirth, and
play ;   farewell pleasure and gay garments, pearls and gems
and all my jewels ;   farewell mantle and scarlet-red, and
my crown ;   farewell hawks and hounds, marks [1] and
bezants,[2] and hunting at the hare and hart and hind for
evermore !   Now will I take the veil and the ring, and
turn anchoress, being still a maiden for thee and for all the
men in Christendom.   For thy sake, squire, I will make
my prayers to Christ ;   and I will never hear Mass but thou
shalt have some part with me, and every day, as long as I
live, thou shalt have thy five Masses, and I will offer three-
pence in token of the Trinity ! "

And while the lady so said in her heavy mourning, she
swooned away.   But her father standing under the wall,
cried out :   " Daughter, ye shall not do so ;   ye must
forego all these vows."

" Alas, father, wellaway !   Now have ye heard what
I said ! "

" Daughter, lay aside your grief, for ye shall be wedded
to a king."

" Certes, father, not for all the gold in Christendom !
Not all the gold God ever made would glad my heart ! "

" My daughter," he said, " my dear darling, I know the

[1] 13s. 4d.   [2] 10s. 6d. to £1.

cause of all your sorrow ! Ye ween that this is the body of your lover ; but, as I live, it is not so ! It was my steward, Sir Maradose,[1] that ye have kept so long hidden."

" Alas, father, how could you let this be ? "

" Because he wrought all your woe. He showed me that he knew your secret, how the squire one day went to your chamber and would have dishonoured you, had he himself not entered with company ; and how you offered the squire gold and goods and a royal force of men. And after, he watched your chamber with bold and sturdy men-at-arms to take him whom you have loved these seven years ; but as he besieged your chamber round about, near midnight came your lover alone, and cried at your door, ' Lady, undo ! ' You bade him wend his way, for there he should get nothing, and as ye thus talked together, came your foes nearer and nearer. They smote at him full soon, thirty to one ; but he pressed into the throng with a stout baslard,[2] and so bare him that he gave them many a wound. Eager and fierce of heart, he cut a-two the steward's throat, whose men then hacked at their master's face, and took and laid him on the marble-stone at your door, where ye might see and think he had been your lover. And presently they overcame the squire, and tore off his fine raiment and put it on the steward, that ye might not know who he was. Thus have you kept your enemy in this place, fading away these seven years. And the squire for

[1] See note.   [2] Hanger.

your sake was seized and thrown into prison, so let be your lamentation, for ye shall be wedded to a king or emperor with gold and silver and great treasure."

"Do away, father, not for all the gold in Christendom! Alas, father, why hath this traitor betrayed me? Alas, great is my wrong in that I have so long kept him here! Alas, father, why did you let this be? Ye might have warned me of my foe! If ye had told me who it was, my love had never died for my sake!" She turned away from the king, and fell a-swooning there.

He went and took her in his two arms. "Daughter," he said, "be of good cheer; your squire lives yet. He hath been in Lombardy and done chivalrous deeds, and is come home again; and ye shall see him in life and health. And he shall wed you, my sweet child. I have made him squire and knight, and he shall be a great lord, and after me wear the crown."

"Father," she cried, "if it be so, let me see him!"

Then he brought in the squire, full fair in life and looks, and as soon as she beheld him, she swooned away; but he caught her in his arms and kissed her an hundred times and more.

There was mirth and melody with harp, psaltery, and gittern,[1] rote,[2] ribibble,[3] and clockard,[4] pipes, organs, and firing of guns; and there were minstrels with zither, and

[1] A sort of guitar.   [2] A small harp.
[3] Prototype of the viol.   [4] For clock, meaning a bell?

song to the psaltery, with fiddle, recorder,[1] and dulcimer,[2] trumpet and clear clarion, and with sweet pipes of many chords—all the lords revelling in the chamber until the morning dawned.

Then said the king to his daughter: "Take here thy love and sweetheart, to live and die with God's blessing. He that would depart you two—God give him sorrow and care! A truer lover than ye are was never flesh and blood; and but he be as true to you, God let him never thrive!"

The king was full merry of heart, and kissed his dear daughter many a time, with melody and good cheer. Anon he called a messenger, and bade him pass to and fro among the cities, and warn his knights to come to Hungary to the wedding and the feast. And so the messenger went, at the king's command, and invited old and young, powerful dukes and earls, and fair ladies.

As soon as ever they heard the cry, these lords made them ready with much mirth and great disport; and with all solemnity on a day the lovers were wedded.

A royal feast was held for dukes and earls and bold barons, for knights and squires, and likewise for all the commonalty of that land. And the story tells that the revels lasted forty days before the king with his twelve chief lords took the squire, and in the hall made him king among them; whereupon all the nobility offered homage.

[1] A kind of flageolet.   [2] Prototype of the piano.

All that day they revelled still, then took leave and went home, each lord to his own land, where he liked best to be.

That young man and his queen lived in great happiness, for, as far as I have gone in the world, never have I seen such lovers!

> *Therefore blest may their souls be!*
> *Amen, amen, for charity!*

NOTES

FLORIS AND BLANCHEFLOUR

This romance (1296 lines) exists in four MSS., all slightly differing and all imperfect. The oldest is the famous Auchinleck MS. in the Advocates' Library, Edinburgh, dated about the first half of the fourteenth century. The poem is supposed to have been written in the second half of the thirteenth century, being the oldest English romance extant which is known to have been translated from a French original. It was modernised by Ellis from a French version differing considerably from the present text. The first edition was made by Lumley for the E.E.T.S. in 1886; and this was re-edited by M'Knight in 1901, for the same society, with three MSS. printed together. In 1885, Hausknecht had already published a critical edition, making use of all the MSS., upon which the present rendering is based.

p. 1. *There was once*, &c. The French text from which the gap is supplied (Du Méril, *Floire et Blanc-flor*, 1856 (A) is certainly not the original of the English version, being a much fuller account, and one differing in many details; but it is believed to be the nearest related among those that have survived. I have omitted its opening lines, which connect the chief figures with the Charlemagne cycle, and further, tell how the poet came to hear the story. As there is nothing to show that these features were in the source of the English poem, I have thought it better to begin with the story itself.

p. 4. *Parchment.* A mark of early date. Paper had not yet been introduced.

p. 6. *Duke Orgas.* The name appears to be the Provençal *Orgeas.* Although this poem was well known in Provence, there is no clear evidence that a Provençal version ever existed.

p. 7. *Carbuncle.* Allusions to the light-giving power of this stone are common. Cf. *Launfal Miles* in the present vol. p. 63, and *The Story of Gray-Steel* in vol. ii., p. 160. The lapidaries note this power, *e.g.* :

> " Scherbuncles gette de sei ráis, . .
> De sa clarté la noit resplent."

p. 9. *Befooling me.* Text, *gabbest*, from O. Fr. *gaber*, to play a practical joke.

p. 12. *Stones of virtue.* It was believed in the Middle Ages that all precious stones influenced for good or evil the health and fortunes of their possessors. The lapidaries related their various properties at great length. Something of this superstition lingers still, especially in regard to the opal, and in the use of coral as a sort of amulet for babies.

p. 16. *My sworn brother.* An allusion to the oath of eternal friendship, which was held most sacred among the Teutons.

p. 17. *Babylon.* This description, notwithstanding its inaccuracies, applies more nearly to ancient Babylon than to Cairo. *Mandeville* distinguishes between the two, and tells something of both, but doubtless they were confused in the popular mind. This poet, by making the King of Nubia one of the emir's vassals, seems to be thinking of Cairo.

p. 18. *The pommel above the leads.* The text is corrupt. One MS. says *kanel*, apparently in the sense of water-pipe, but as these conduits are described later, and the context seems to refer to the roof, I have chosen the alternative reading *kernel* = battlements. Then the sense of the passage is apparently that, above the leads, *i.e.*, on the roof, the battlements are adorned with golden balls.

p. 18. *Never wish for Paradise.* An allusion to the Mohammedan *peris*?

p. 18. *Middle Earth.* Expresses the old Teutonic conception of earth as the middle home, *i.e.*, between the dwellings of the gods and of the powers of evil.

p. 18. *A stone wherein*, &c., *i.e.*, by crystal-gazing.

SIR ORPHEO

This lay (602 lines) is found in four MSS., of which the Auchinleck is again the oldest. One was printed by Ritson, in his *Ancient Engleish Metrical Romanceës*, 1802; a second by Laing, *Select Remains of the Ancient Popular Poetry of Scotland*, 1822; the third by Halliwell in his *Illustrations of the Fairy Mythology of A Midsummer Night's Dream*, 1845; while a separate critical edition, made by Zielke in 1880, MS. Digby, 86, is still unpublished. In a study in the *American Journal of Philology*, vol. viii., Prof. Kittredge points out the Celtic modifications of the classic myth. Although the original of this poem is lost, it is undoubtedly a translation. A French *lai* of *Orphée* is several times referred to in the twelfth century.

p. 32. *Orfeo.* A claim has been made for an Italian source on the strength of this form, but other evidence is lacking.

p. 32. *Of lays*, &c. The introduction which I have here kept in verse is found almost identical in the *Lay of the Ash*, p. 47, where I have rendered the text into prose. It is impossible to say with certainty for which poem, if for either, it was originally intended. The presumption is in favour of *Orfeo*, in that nothing of the sort occurs in the French original of the *Lay of the Ash*.

p. 33. *King Juno.* Doubtless the *o* was evidence of masculinity to this scribe. The Harley MS. says that Orfeo's parents were Pilato and Yno.

p. 34. *Traciens.* The Auchinleck MS. adds a couplet to the effect that Winchester was so called formerly.

p. 34. *Under a fair imp-tree.* *Cf.* Child's *Ballads* (1886), vol. i., 340, for references to the supposed danger of falling asleep under special trees, usually fruit-trees, and among them, the apple. In Greek superstition, summer-noon is the most dangerous season.

p. 40. *Rode into a rock.* The Celtic Other-World was reached sometimes across the sea, again through a dense forest, and still again, as here, through a cavern. For references, see Kittredge's article mentioned above. The rock entrance is found also in Teutonic and in classical mythology.

p. 41. *Without . . . hill or dale.* According to medieval ideas, this was a beautiful landscape. What we call picturesque country was at that time associated with terror of supernatural creatures, and sometimes of lawless human beings.

p. 41. *As bright as the noonday sun.* In the Middle Ages gems were commonly supposed to be a source of light. See the note on *carbuncle-stone*, p. 179.

p. 41. *Thought to be dead,* &c. The fairies were commonly looked upon as dethroned pagan gods, who were therefore active for evil. Chaucer called Pluto king of the fairies. Like the devils, with whom they are sometimes confused, they have power under certain conditions, as, for instance, over people who have forgotten to protect themselves by the sign of the cross, though that is not indicated in this poem. The description of the victims shows little if any influence from the classical conception of Hades.

p. 42. *Where we be unwelcome.* A singularly vivid touch,

showing the trials of the wandering minstrel even at that early date.

p. 44. *A harper of heathendom.* The pagan Orpheus here becomes a Christian king pretending to be a pagan.

LAY OF THE ASH

This exists in incomplete form in the Auchinleck MS. only. It was published by Weber in his *Metrical Romances*, 1810, under the title *Lai le Freine*, and later, in *Anglia*, vol. iii. It is a fairly close rendering of *Le Fraisne* by Marie de France; and I have supplied the missing portions immediately from her text, instead of using Weber's metrical reconstruction on the basis of the French, although this continues the tale in very much the style of the beginning.

p. 50. *A wild heath.* The little scraps of nature and country life are due largely to the English poet.

LAUNFAL MILES

This lay (1044 lines) is found only in MS. Cotton Caligula A ii., dating probably between 1446 and 1460. It was published by Ritson in his collection mentioned above. Another version called *Landavall* was published and studied by Prof. Kittredge in the *American Journal of Philology*, vol. x., and a third called *Sir Lambewell*, printed first in 1558, is to be found in Hales and Furnivall's edition of the Percy Folio MS. The source of all three, and of two fragmentary versions, is the *Lanval* of Marie de France, from which the version here modernised diverges most widely (containing more than 300 additional lines), by introducing other material. This version was composed by one Thomas Chestre, whose name is found in the last stanza, not earlier than the latter part of the fourteenth century.

p. 57. *Miles.* *Soldier,* hence *knight;* here, equivalent to *Sir.*

p. 57. *Carlisle.* Text: *Kardeuyle* = Cardeuil or Carduil, which is generally held to refer to Carlisle; and here is apparently distinct from Caerleon, with which it is sometimes identified. Again, however, all three names are found together.

p. 57. *Knights of the Round Table.* Nearly all mentioned here are familiar through Malory's *Morte d'Arthur,* and Tennyson's *Idylls of the King.* Sir Percival is the hero of the English metrical romance, *Sir Perceval of Galles,* which seems to be a more antique form of the tale than Chrétien de Troyes' poem on the same theme; he appears also in the Welsh *Mabinogion* as Peredur. He is the uncouth, rustic hero who surprised Arthur's court by his achievements, very different from Tennyson's conception of him in *The Holy Grail.* Sir Gawayn, the secondary hero in the great *Conte du Graal* begun by Chrétien de Troyes as *Perceval le Gallois* without knowledge of the Grail episode, was, through this book and translations and adaptations of portions of it, a familiar figure in Middle English, especially in the North, where his name survives still (Gavin). He was pre-eminently the knight courteous, and by no means the fickle, untrustworthy being described by Tennyson. He and the less-known Gaheris and Agravayne, sometimes called *le Orgueilleux,* were the sons of King Lot of Orkney and King Arthur's sister Bellicent. Gaheris is the Gareth of Tennyson's *Gareth and Lynette,* and Agravayne lends his name, under the form Degrevant (*cf.* note on p. 187 below), to a Middle English romance included in this volume. Lancelot du Lake gradually superseded Gawayne as the chief knight of the Round Table. He is the hero of Chrétien's *Roman de la Charrette,* and of the prose *Lancelot* attributed to Walter Map, translated into Scotch in the fifteenth century under the title, *Lancelot of the Laik.* He was the son of King Ban of Benwick in France, mentioned below as Ban-Booght. The second part of the last name is evidently another spelling, as is also the *Bos* which follows it, of *Bors*, *Boort*, the name of Ban's brother. Kay is one of the oldest of the Arthurian heroes, being mentioned in the Welsh *Triads*. In the earlier traditions he figured as a powerful knight (*cf.* his appearance in the *Story of Gray-Steel*, vol. ii., p. 154, of this series), but later, he became the laughing-stock of the minstrels. He was Arthur's seneschal. Ywain is the hero of Chrétien's *Chevalier au Lion*, translated into Middle English as *Iwain and Gawin*. Galafre I have not identified. Ritson suggests *Galahad;* but the name is nearer to the French *Gaufrei* (Galfridus = Geoffrey), who, however, belonged to the *geste* of Doon de Mayence. Launfal (Fr. Lanval) does not seem to appear elsewhere. The name only has been borrowed by Lowell in his *Sir Launfal*.

p. 58. *Merlin*, the magician, was Arthur's chief counsellor, one of the most familiar figures in medieval literature. He is prominent in various French romances, and appears in Middle English in a very early poem called *Arthour and Merlin*, and later in Lovelich's *Merlin*. See also Tennyson's *Merlin and Vivien*.

p. 58. *King Ryence* or *Ryon*. King of Ireland and North Wales, who, in some stories, sent to King Arthur a demand for his beard to make the twelfth for fringing his own mantle. He is sometimes represented as the enemy against whom Arthur helps Guinevere's father, Leodogran; only here, as far as I remember, as her father.

p. 59. *Caerleon*. In Monmouthshire. *Urbs Legionum.* Near it is a Roman camp known locally as King Arthur's Round Table.

p. 60. *Glastonbury*. Associated with the name of Arthur after the reported discovery of his tomb there in the twelfth century. It came to be identified with the Isle of Avalon, to which he was supposed to have been conveyed mortally wounded; thence, legend had it, he should one day return in time of need.

p. 62. *Snow on the downs.* An uncommon figure, showing that Chestre was used to a hill country.

p. 63. *Dame Tryamour.* The pun is probably intentional, *try-amour*, i.e., *test-love*, such hybrids of French and English occurring elsewhere. A similar name is Lufamour (*love-amour*, perhaps for *love par amour*), in *Sir Perceval of Galles.* In the romance of *Sir Triamour*, the name is given to a man, and seems to be used without special significance.

p. 63. *Saracen work.* This was supreme praise. Saracen work became known especially through the conquest of Sicily by the Normans, who encouraged and exploited the silk-weaving that they found there. After the Sicilian Vespers in 1282, these Saracen weavers carried their industry into Italy, whence it spread throughout Europe. The romances are rich in allusions to the beauty of this work.

p. 63. *Olyroun.* Possibly confused with *Oberon.* See note on p. 79 above, where the name is given correctly to an island.

p. 64. *Blaunchard.* Probably white, as the name suggests. The supernatural horse in *Sir Amadas* (vol. ii.) was white; and so were the fairies' horses in *Sir Orfeo.*

p. 64. *Gyfre.* Ritson pointed out the resemblance between this name and *Giflet* or *Girflet*, in the French *Lancelot du Lac*; but it is practically the same as *Giffroun* (*le Fludus*), in *Lybeaus Disconus.*

p. 64. *No knight's blow shall hurt thee.* In *Floris and Blanche-flour* this protection and more was given by a ring (*cf.* p. 12, above).

p. 67. *Earl of Chester . . . Welsh knights.* The last of the old Earls of Chester died 1237, but as the tournament does not appear in Marie's poem, this earl, and the Welsh knights who seem to have been of his party, must have been introduced by Chestre, whose name probably denotes some connection with the town of Chester. Curiously enough, the title Earl of Chester was revived in 1376, and conferred upon the young prince, afterwards Richard II. It is possible that in this added passage there is a touch of local colour taken from Chestre's own experience; but further evidence is needed as to the origin of the poem before the point can be explained.

p. 68. *A knight in Lombardy*, &c. This episode is peculiar to Chestre's version; but may well have been borrowed from some other romance.

p. 69. *Striped cloth, i.e., ray*, which is often mentioned, especially in the fourteenth century.

p. 70. *Gave it back to his lord.* Being a fairy, Gyfre was invisible.

p. 73. *Break in three.* The use of numbers in the Middle Ages is a study in itself. *Three* was common in token of the Trinity; *five*, of the five wounds of Christ, &c.

p. 75. *Earl of Cornwall.* The Duke of Cornwall was introduced by Marie; and again in the fourteenth century the Black Prince and his son, Richard II., were both created, not Earls, but Dukes of Cornwall.

THE EARL OF TOULOUSE

This romance (1218 lines) exists in four MSS., two of the fifteenth and two of the early sixteenth century. It was included by Ritson in his collection, and edited separately, with a detailed study of its sources, by Lüdtke, Berlin, 1881. *Cf.* Child's *Ballads* (1886), ii., 33 ff., for parallels. It is supposed to be a translation of a lost *lai*.

p. 89. *Kantres* and *Kaym*. The character given to the knights suggests that *Kaym* is used, as elsewhere sometimes, for *Cain*. But the whole phrase may be a corruption. Cf. *Kay of Kaynes* (vol. ii., p. 184). *Kantres* I have not identified.

p. 98. *Sir Antore.* Possibly derived from the word *aunter* = *adventure* (*cf.* the assumed name *Anterous* in *Sir Degrevant*). A Sir Antore occurs in *Lybeaus Disconus.*

SIR DEGREVANT

This romance (1904 lines) is found in the famous Thornton MS., dated about the middle of the fifteenth century, and in one other of about the same date. It was edited first by Halliwell, with three others, under the title *The Thornton Romances,* for the Camden Society, 1844, and was reprinted by F. S. Ellis, Kelmscott Press, 1896. No French original is known.

p. 106. *Nephew to the King.* He is certainly Agravaine, son of King Lot of Orkney and Arthur's sister Bellicent. An alternative spelling, fairly common, is *Egrevain.* Assuming that this name once formed part of the title of a French poem such as *Lai* or *Roman d'Egrevaint,* we can see how the *d'* might have come to be regarded as a part of the name, especially as the *de* was not invariably kept in the title. For example, we find *Lai le Freine.* The same process doubtless accounts for the similar name *Degarre* = *d'Egaré* (*Lai d'Egaré?*), the pronunciation of which is shown by the later spelling *Degree.*

The only other mention I have found of an Arthurian knight called Degrevant, is in one of the MSS. of John Harding's *Chronicle,* xlviii. ff. (*cf. Introduction,* p. xlviii. ff.). The story itself has nothing or very little to do with King Arthur, but has been attached to his name to keep it in the fashion.

p. 107. *Mappa Mundi.* *Cf.* Chaucer's: "As fer as cercled is the mappemounde." See *Introduction, loc. cit.*

p. 107. *True as the anchor in a stone;* *i.e.,* as true to himself as the anchor to its nature when it drops among the stones?

p. 108. *Granada.* So Chaucer's knight: "In Gernade at the seege eek hadde he be."

p. 109. *Sir Sere of Cypirs.* This name occurs in one MS. only, and suggests a French original; but the phrase is obviously corrupt. The place is perhaps Cyprus. The name Sir Sasere is found on the Winchester Round Table.

p. 111. *Heathery hills.* Text: *hethene*, which can scarcely mean anything but *heath-en*.

p. 112. *With their kinsfolk.* Text: *Kene kyneghus in-with kyth.* A possible allusion to the clan ?

p. 113. *Barbary horse.* Text: *Steed ferraunt.* Common in the romances.

p. 115. *Knights-banneret.* Landowners, who therefore were qualified to have a banner and to summon vassals to the field, in distinction from *knights-bachelor*, who were landless.

p. 116. *Melidore's.* The name is French; *cf.* Froissart's *Méliador.*

p. 116. *Rhine-gold.* A clear allusion to the *Nibelungenlied*, or some other form of the same tradition, in which the accursed hoard of gold is at last sunk in the Rhine. This is the only reference that I remember in English literature of that time.

p. 117. *Castle nor town.* Text: *broch nor by*—a peculiarly Northern phrase. *Broch* is now applied especially to ruins attributed to the so-called "Picts," and *by* is the generic name, of Scandinavian origin, for town, surviving only in compounds such as Kirkby Stephen, *i.e.*, the town of the church of Stephen.

p. 118. *Violet.* According to the Thornton MS., she was dressed in violet pall, according to the Lincoln, in purple velvet. The description of her costume is so confused that I have pieced the two MSS. together to make a connected account.

p. 120. *Pink.* Text: *periwinkle.* In flower-lore, the peri-winkle was supposed to inspire love; hence, perhaps the phrase.

p. 122. *Duke of Gerle.* Gueldres? But he is a Frenchman.

p. 123. *Moat.* Text: *water-wall.* It cannot be a waterfall, as Halliwell translates, because the context explains clearly that it was filled and emptied by the tide: therefore it is probably a moat.

p. 125. *Background of black.* I guess at the meaning. The Thornton MS. says: "Hys bagges this blake;" the Lincoln MS.: "Bot his bagges are blake." In both cases, the spelling *blake* looks more like the Norse word meaning *pale;* but that does not help the sense. *Bagges* are sometimes bagpipes; but here the question is of a shield.

p. 126. *Stack.* A Norse word meaning anything fixed firmly, as a hay-*stack.* In Shetland the word survives with the meaning, an isolated rock at sea. The modern "firm as a rock" suggests that this is the usage here.

p. 126. *Out of the west.* The phrase is not uncommon; but here, as the scene is in the North Country, may well allude to the south-western part of Scotland, whence came so many raiders. *Cf.* the "wild men of the west," p. 131.

p. 128. *Toptelers.* The French *toupet, topet* means the tuft of hair on a horse's forehead; hence, there may have been a derivative (not in Godefroy's dictionary, however), from which came *topteler* (*topetelier?*), in the sense, ornament for the *topet.*

p. 129. *Of war or of jousting, i.e.,* with or without iron heads, according to the intent of the knights, whether they engage through hostility or in a mere trial of strength.

p. 130. *Sir Anterous.* Evidently Degrevant in disguise; but the text is confused. Later, Melidore calls him by that name, which is suitable enough, as it means *adventurous*.

p. 132. *Aylsham towels*. Linen manufacture at Aylsham, Norfolk, began in the reign of Edward III.

p. 132. *The room*, &c. This very detailed description of a room, with its many French words, suggests a French original, and the French romances were much given to this sort of elaboration.

p. 133. *Archangels in red gold*. Probably carved corbels.

p. 133. *Clock*. Text: *orrelegge* (Fr. *horologe*), first quoted from 1381, in N. E. D. This allusion at least seems due to the English minstrel.

p. 133. *Little horns*. Text: *moynels* = O. Fr. *moienels*. I don't know what it means here unless it refers to tracery.

p. 133. *Agate*. Text: *geete* = jet. The extensive use of jet for walls is improbable. The minstrel has possibly confused *achate*, *agathe* = agate, with *gagate* = jet.

p. 133. *Godfrey de Bouillon*. An historical hero of the First Crusade, and the legendary hero to whom was attached the cycle of the Swan-children, of which *Lohengrin* is a familiar version.

p. 133. *Amadas and Ydoyne*. Famous lovers in the Middle Ages, concerning whom a thirteenth-century French romance still survives. They were often alluded to in Middle English, but there is no trace of an English romance on that theme. *Sir Amadas* in volume ii. is a different story. These lovers made one of four groups embroidered on the famous cloth that became the wedding-dress in the romance of *Emaré*.

p. 133. *Popinjays*. This design seems to have been fashionable, as it is mentioned several times also in *The Squire of Low Degree*.

p. 133. *Tasselled bags*. One or two large bags usually appear, in medieval pictures of beds, hanging inside the curtains and made of the same stuff. Their use I do not know, unless it would be to hold articles of apparel, which always in such pictures seem to be put away.

p. 133. *Westphalia*. This, with the preceding allusion to the Rhine-gold, hints at an acquaintance with Germany not common in the works of that time.

p. 134. *Mermaidens' hair*. Halliwell adopts the reading that Melidore and her "merry maidens" had spun the cords won by Duke Betys; but in that case, we are not told of what they were made, or why he should trouble to win them. The comparison of hair to "gold wires" is common in the romances; and here it seems probable that we have allusion to some lost story in which a knight brings home mermaids' hair, which was of the actual stuff of gold.

p. 135. *Sir Eymour* (later, *Eymere*) *the Kayous*. The name is either *Emere* (pronounced *Emère*) or *Aylmer*. *Kay* is still dialectical for *left* (hand or foot), so *Kayous* would seem to mean *left-handed*.

THE KNIGHT OF COURTESY AND THE FAIR LADY OF FAGUELL

This romance (500 lines) is written in the ballad stanza, and indeed is almost an intermediate form between romance and ballad. No MS. of it is known. It was edited by Ritson from a unique printed book now in the Bodleian library, issued by William Copland before 1568. It is a version, derived, one would say, judging by its lack of proper names and by its general vagueness, from some popular form of the French legend of the Seigneur de Coucy and the Dame de Faïel.

This was told at great length in a French romance of the thirteenth century, which deals with historical personages.

p. 145. *Rhodes.* The allusion to the fighting at Rhodes could scarcely have been written before 1443. In this year the Templars called upon the Pope to summon help for the defence of that island, which was then besieged by the Sultan of Turkey. The change of scene from the Holy Land in the French versions, to Rhodes in the English, seems to show both that the poet was not acquainted with his original in detail, and that his poem was not written long before 1450.

p. 147. *Towards Good Friday.* The heathen were always supposed, in the romances, to make special efforts to overthrow their enemies on Christian holy days.

p. 149. *Great noise of guns.* But rarely mentioned, and only in the later romances. Cf. *Squire of Low Degree*, p. 175.

p. 151. *Dress me anon this heart*, &c. For parallel tales of a woman forced to eat her lover's heart, *cf.* Child's *Ballads* (1886), vol. v., 29.

THE SQUIRE OF LOW DEGREE

A late form of this romance (1132 lines) is contained in the Percy Folio MS. It was licensed in 1560 to be printed. A text by Copland and fragments of another by Wynkyn de Worde have survived. The poem was included by Ritson in his collection, and published separately by W. E. Mead in 1904. It possibly suggested to Spenser his Squire of Low Degree; and Shakespeare probably refers to the poem in his Henry V. "You called me yesterday mountain-squire, but I will make you to-day a squire of low degree!" No French original is known; but the poem contains an unusually large proportion of uncommon French words not taken over by English.

p. 153. *Fairest trees*, &c. This author is peculiarly fond of lists, and begins with trees, shrubs, and plants of both hot and temperate climates, jumbled all together.

p. 153. *First chosen by Jesus*, *i.e.*, in the Cross. According to Sir John Mandeville, cypress was one of the four woods of which the cross was made; but some legend may have named cypress alone.

p. 153. *Laverock*, &c. The popinjay or parrot is the only bird not found in England, the peacock of course having been imported, and the author's list is much more extensive than usual.

p. 154. *Sir Guy . . . Colbrand.* Guy of Warwick, in the romance of that name, overcame the Danish giant Colbrand, whose name still survives in the village of Cockburnspath (formerly spelled Colbrandspath), on the east coast of Scotland near Dunbar.

p. 157. *On three Good Fridays*, *i.e.*, for three years, in honour of the Trinity, to meet the assaults of the heathen, which reach their climax on Good Friday, as being one of the great days in the Christian faith.

p. 157. *Gold and gules set with sable.* In heraldry, gules is red, and sable is black, being really a fine network of horizontal and perpendicular lines.

p. 157. *Amor.* So Chaucer's Prioress wore the motto: "*Amor vincit omnia*"—love conquers all.

p. 158. *Bear it to the Sepulchre*, &c. In the pictorial life of the Earl of Warwick (the King-maker), with drawings by Richard Rous, is a sketch that shows him offering up his arms similarly.

p. 158. *Wheel of Victory.* A confusion with Fortune's Wheel, conceived, in the Middle Ages, as having men clinging to its spokes, and so going up and down as it revolved.

p. 159. *Dainty meats.* Peacock was a great delicacy. Of the

I.

others named, the stork was perhaps the most uncommon, even at that time, as an article of food.

p. 160. *Since he was young.* Text reads *I* ; but this would make the squire the king's contemporary, which is contrary to the sense of the passage.

p. 162. *Summoned all the officers.* The marshal had supreme authority in the hall and kitchen, even over the cook, whether the latter were "lief or loth."

p. 165. *Sir Libius.* An allusion to the popular romance of *Lybeaus Disconus.* The details, however, differ from those in any known version, although the general course of the story is similar.

p. 168. *Romney,* &c. *Romney* is sometimes thought to have been a Greek wine ; but Dr. Furnivall holds that it was Italian. *Malmsey, bastard,* and *muscadel* were all mixed with honey, the first originally Greek, the second Corsican, the third French. *Pyment* was a general term for a mixture of wine, honey, and spices. *Hippocras* was an elaborate concoction of the same sort, named from a bag of peculiar shape through which it was strained, "Hippocrates' sleeve." *Vernage* was a red Tuscan wine. Greek wines are often mentioned, and were much imported, especially from Candia. *Rochelle* came from the French town of that name, *Osey* from Alsace, *Antioch* from that city, *Gernade* from Granada, *Algrade* from Algarde in Spain. Mount Rose = *couleur de rose,* some red wine ? *Respice* = *raspice,* made from unbruised grapes with their stalks fermented in other wine. The word suggests *raspberries* (*rasps*).

p. 169. *Robes of the same silk.* Text : *sickles . . .* of *taffetras. Sickles* looks like a corruption of Latin *cyclas* = a tunic, which in turn was confused sometimes with Fr. *ciclatoun,* rich silky stuff. *Taffetras* I take to be merely a corruption of *taffeta.* Perhaps the allusion is to the surplices of the choir ?

p. 169. *Counternote and descant.* The first is *counterpoint*, the second, its predecessor, a kind of melody used to accompany *plainsong.*

p. 169. *Arras cloth.* N. E. D. quotes first from 1397. By Shakespeare's time the word had become a common noun meaning only *tapestry*, so well known were the productions from that town.

p. 169. *Bowls.* The first mention of this in N. E. D. is quoted from Occleve, 1420.

p. 170. *A barge shall meet you*, &c. Henry VI. was conveyed to Westminster in a barge instead of by a state procession on land; and doubtless his choice encouraged the fashion of this mode of progression. The passage reads like a description of a pleasure-trip down the Thames as far as the sea.

p. 170. *Hey, how*, &c. The refrain of an old sea-song several times quoted at this period, as in Skelton's *Bowge of Court*, in *Cock Lorell*, and by Fabyan in a song on Bannockburn. It is said to have been composed by watermen on the occasion of Henry VI.'s water-procession alluded to above; but a song with that refrain is mentioned about 1300 in the romance of *Richard Cœur de Lion* (l. 2522).

p. 170. *Costards.* The sense is doubtful. Apparently they were a part of the bed. The word means *apples*, hence *balls*. Perhaps some kind of ball-ornament similar to Fr. *pommel* (derived from *pomme*, which also means *apple*, *ball*) is referred to. The word *pommel* was carried over into English, but it may have suggested *costard* to this author, because of the similar root-idea.

p. 170. *Bed-posts.* A guess for *felyoles*, which seems to be Fr. *fillole, filloelle*, meaning pillars.

p. 171. *Long-pepper.* Sir John Mandeville in his *Travels* has an observation on different kinds of pepper, including this, which is more rarely used than black or white (ed. 1900, Macmillan, pp. 112, 113).

p. 174. *Sir Maradose.* In the romance of *Sir Triamour* (Percy Folio MS.), one Marradas is fought by the hero; but if the name was borrowed from the source, it was probably confused by the borrower with *Marrocke*, which was the name of a false steward who betrayed his lord's daughter.